D0510486

PUZZLE CASTLE

793.
73
LEI

Contents

About this story

This story is about a brave knight called Sophie and her adventure at Puzzle Castle. There is a puzzle on every double page. Solve them all and help Sophie on her way. If you get stuck, look at the answers on pages 31 and 32.

This is Sophie, the brave knight. She lives in a village not far from Puzzle Castle.

This is Puzzle Castle.

Sophie's friend, Titus the Timid, lives in Puzzle Castle. He has written Sophie a letter. Here it is.

Puzzle Castle
Monday

Dear Sophie,

You are invited to a grand banquet in Puzzle Castle today, but first we need your help. For the past three days there has been a monster in the dungeons. No one has seen it, but everyone is very scared. You are the bravest person I know. Could you come early and get rid of it? I will meet you in the castle courtyard at three o'clock.

Love from your friend, Titus.

P.S. I will be wearing my banquet outfit!

This is Titus. He is wearing his banquet outfit.

Useful equipment

When Sophie gets to the castle she will need to find ten things that may come in handy when she reaches the dungeons. You will find one object on every double page, from the moment she enters the castle, until she arrives at the monster's lair...

Cecil the castle ghost

Puzzle Castle is haunted by a very friendly ghost. His name is Cecil. He is hiding spookily on every double page. See if you can spot him.

Jester Jim

Jester Jim is practising his juggling for the banquet, but he's not very good at it. He has lost his juggling balls around the castle. There is at least one hiding on every double page.
Can you find them?

The juggling balls look like this.

The adventure starts

On the day of the grand banquet, Sophie set out for Puzzle Castle. As she drew near, the castle loomed ahead of her, surrounded by a monstrous moat. Peering down into the water she saw strange creatures and big fish with snappy teeth.

The only way across the water was by the many bridges. But this wasn't as easy as it looked. Some of the bridges were broken and others were too dangerous to cross. Sophie would have to be very careful.

Can you find a safe route across the moat?

Start looking out for Cecil!
Don't forget to look out for Jim's juggling balls!

Where is Titus?

Sophie jumped to the safety of the bank. She bounded up to the castle gate and pulled the bell which jangled loudly. The gate rose slowly and Sophie stepped into the bustling courtyard of Puzzle Castle.

Everyone was busy preparing for the grand banquet and trying hard not to think about the monster in the dungeons. It was nearly three o'clock. Sophie looked out for Titus. She was sure he was hiding somewhere.

Can you see Titus?

grrrr!
boo!

Sophie's instructions

"Don't worry, Titus, I'll deal with the monster," said Sophie bravely. "Lead me to the dungeons."

"Oh no, Sophie," Titus shivered. "You are brave enough to find the monster by yourself. Here's a plan of Puzzle Castle, and a list of people you will meet on your journey. You must visit each person in turn. Each one needs your help getting ready for the banquet. Help them out and you will soon find your way to the dungeons."

Can you match the people with the rooms where Sophie is most likely to find them?

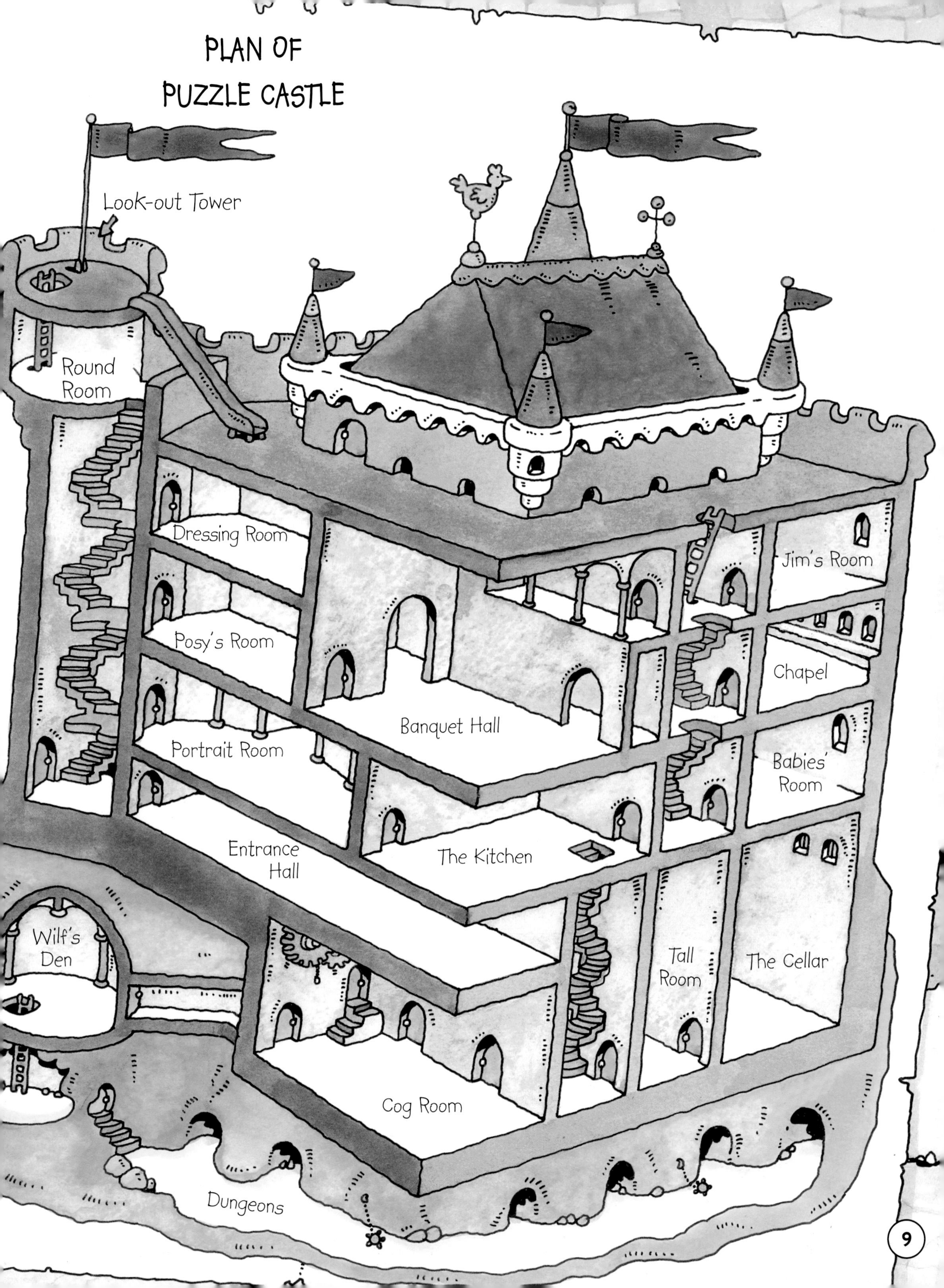
PLAN OF
PUZZLE CASTLE
Look-out Tower
Round Room
Dressing Room
Posy's Room
Portrait Room
Entrance Hall
Banquet Hall
The Kitchen
Jim's Room
Chapel
Babies' Room
Wilf's Den
Tall Room
The Cellar
Cog Room
Dungeons

Royal portraits

Sophie promised to see Titus later and began her journey. Her first stop was the portrait gallery.

"Sophie," cried Mervin the portrait keeper. "Princess Posy's Uncle Edwin is coming all the way from Gruldavia for the banquet. I have to meet him, but I've forgotten what he looks like. If I get this wrong, I'll be thrown in the dungeons. His picture is here. He has black hair, a beard and a moustache. He always wears red and purple. He has no children and he doesn't like horses."

Can you find Uncle Edwin's picture?

Princess Posy's problem

Sophie curtsied as she entered Princess Posy's room. What a mess it was!

"Sophie!" cried Posy. "I know you're going to fight the monster, but I've got a bigger problem. I want to wear my matching necklace, bracelet, ring and crown to the banquet. I can't find them in my big wooden chest."

Can you find a necklace, a bracelet, a ring and a crown that match?

MUM and DAD
UNCLE EDWIN
QUEEN

The look-out tower

Sophie left Posy admiring her jewels, and climbed up to the castle battlements. Here she found Larry the look-out boy, pointing to a lot of people approaching the castle.

"Sophie!" he cried. "All these people are arriving for the grand banquet, but I don't know if they've been invited."

Sophie read the guest list. Then she looked at the flags of the approaching groups and checked to see if they were invited or not.

Do you know who is invited to the banquet?

Beth and the babies

Sophie scrambled down to the babies' room. Here she found Beth, the very new babysitter, and lots of naughty babies.

"Sophie," cried Beth. "I have to dress the babies for the banquet, but I don't know which clothes belong to which baby. I've even forgotten each baby's name!"

Sophie looked at the party outfits hanging on the wall. Then she looked at the babies in their underwear. Soon she had matched them together.

Can you find the right outfit for each baby?

Freya
Joe
Bed time is at 7 p.m.
BEtH
Amber
Kezi
Jack
George
Yeah!
Pretty
Hee hee!

In the kitchen

Sophie left Beth with the smartly dressed babies and followed the smell of burned banquet buns to the kitchen. The grand banquet feast was boiling away, but Mrs. Crumb the cook was flustered.

"I wanted to make you a monster-fighting pudding to build up your strength, Sophie," she said. "But some rascal has hidden the ingredients. I've lost two red plums, a pot of honey, three fresh eggs, four loaves of bread and a lemon."

Can you find the missing pudding ingredients?

COOKIES
biscuits
Mustard

Which way now?

"I'll have to eat that pudding later!" Sophie called, as she dropped through the trapdoor. She climbed down some steep steps. To the right was a door. She pushed it open and walked into a room with cogs hanging from the ceiling. There was no one here, so Sophie decided to move on.

Her next stop was Wizard Wilf's den. But which door led to it? There were six to choose from, but danger lurked behind almost every one. Sophie looked at her castle plan and soon knew which door to take.

Which door should Sophie choose?

COAL

The wizard's den

Sophie pushed open the door and walked down a small passageway to another door. Through this door lay Wizard Wilf's secret den. Wilf stood stirring a big pot.

"Sophie," he cried. "I'm brewing a magic potion to cast a spell. It will make you invisible and help you dodge the monster."

Sophie held her breath as Wilf waved his magic wand. There was a purple flash and a puff of smoke, but when it had cleared they saw the spell hadn't quite worked. Sophie was still there, but lots of other things had vanished.

How many things have disappeared? Can you spot them all?

Sophie finds the way

There was no time to waste. Sophie climbed down Wilf's ladder and crept along an underground passageway. She soon found herself at the beginning of a maze of tunnels. In the distance she could hear the terrible roars of the monster. She didn't want to get lost underground as she made her way towards the roars, so she unravelled her ball of useful string as she went.

Can you find the way to the monster's roars?

moan!
roar!

The monster's lair...

The rumbling and roaring noise grew louder as Sophie reached the end of the maze. She was at the top of a small flight of steps.

Sophie checked she had all her equipment with her. Chewing nervously on an extra-brave toffee, Sophie began her final journey, down the winding staircase to the monster's lair...

She checked her monster phrase book.
Hello. Are you a friendly monster?
Og gob glook?
Where's the station?
Zip zap zop?
She turned the key.
She opened the door and saw...
...a little dragon, crying and sniffing. Was this the fierce monster of Puzzle Castle? Could Sophie cheer him up?
Hello...hic...sob. My name's Dennis. I got stuck in this scary dungeon. I'm hungry and cold and I've lost my mum.
MUM
Then she remembered. She could give him the one piece of equipment she hadn't used yet.
What can Sophie give Dennis?

The grand banquet

Dennis cheered up at once. Then Sophie had another idea. She would take him to the banquet. Sophie led Dennis back through the castle and up to the grand banquet hall.

At first everyone was scared of Dennis. But they soon saw he wasn't a monster at all. He was a very friendly little dragon who liked to dance. Everyone was very pleased to see him.

There is someone in this picture who is especially happy to see Dennis. Do you know who it is?

Bedtime story

After the banquet, everyone was very tired. Just before bedtime, Sophie, Titus and Posy curled up with their cups of castle cocoa and listened as Dennis told the story of his adventure at Puzzle Castle...

On Saturday I was playing on the hill beside Puzzle Castle.

Suddenly I saw Boris the Bad and his baddies coming my way. I was very scared.

I saw a tunnel in the hill and I hid inside.

Boris's army pounded past. The ground shook.

Heavy earth fell in front of the tunnel. I was trapped inside.

I could only go on, deeper into the tunnel, until I reached the castle dungeon.

I was there for three days, getting hungrier and hungrier, until Sophie rescued me.

I'll never forget the friends I made today.

Answers

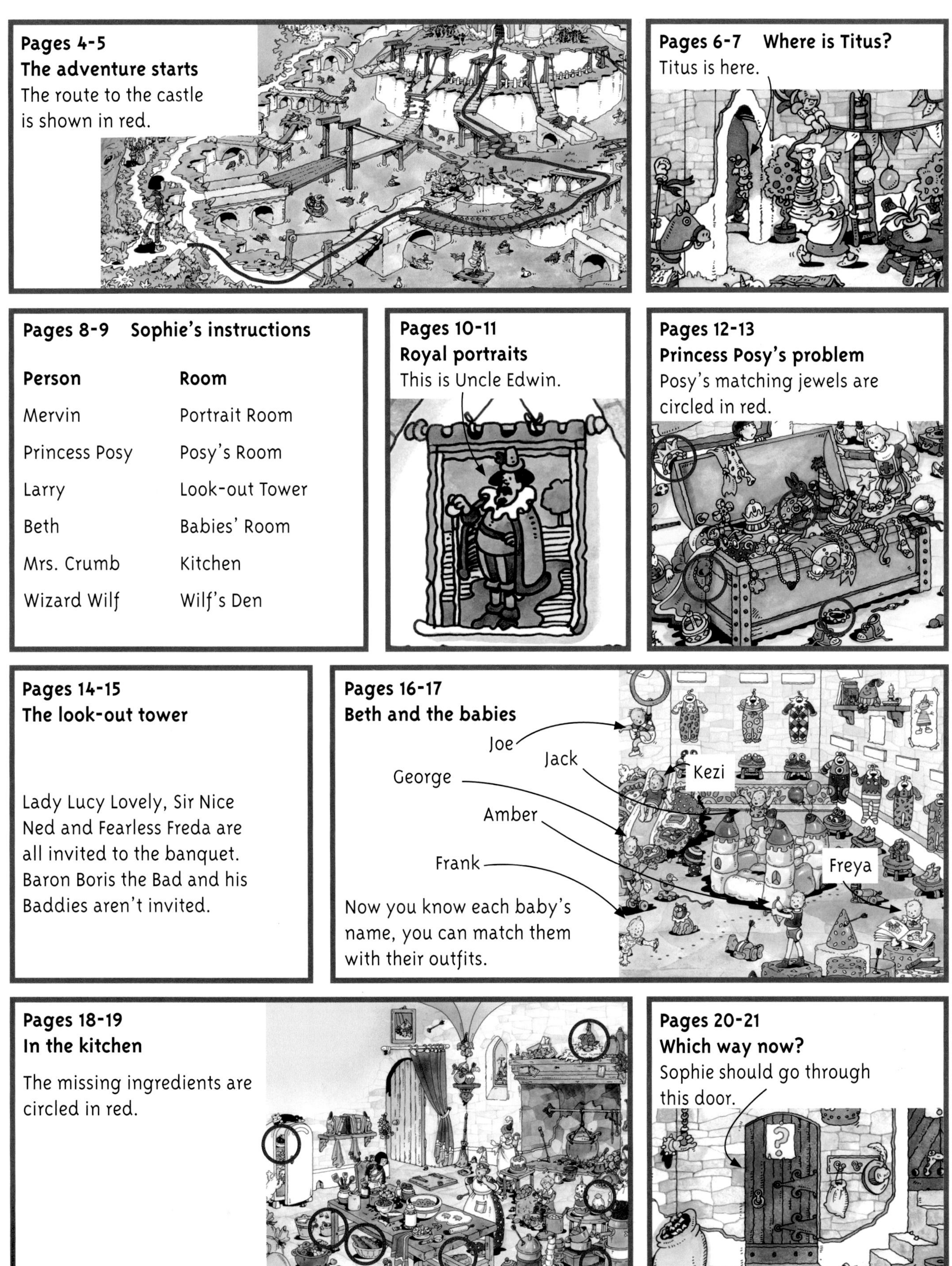

Pages 4-5
The adventure starts

The route to the castle is shown in red.

Pages 6-7 Where is Titus?

Titus is here.

Pages 8-9 Sophie's instructions

Person	Room
Mervin	Portrait Room
Princess Posy	Posy's Room
Larry	Look-out Tower
Beth	Babies' Room
Mrs. Crumb	Kitchen
Wizard Wilf	Wilf's Den

Pages 10-11
Royal portraits

This is Uncle Edwin.

Pages 12-13
Princess Posy's problem

Posy's matching jewels are circled in red.

Pages 14-15
The look-out tower

Lady Lucy Lovely, Sir Nice Ned and Fearless Freda are all invited to the banquet. Baron Boris the Bad and his Baddies aren't invited.

Pages 16-17
Beth and the babies

Now you know each baby's name, you can match them with their outfits.

Pages 18-19
In the kitchen

The missing ingredients are circled in red.

Pages 20-21
Which way now?

Sophie should go through this door.

Pages 22-23
The wizard's den
The red circles show where Wilf's things were.

Pages 24-25
Sophie finds the way
The way to the monster is shown in red.

Pages 26-27
The monster's lair...
Sophie gives Dennis the mystery box she found in the wizard's den. It is a dragon-in-a-box!

Pages 28-29
The grand banquet
Dennis's mum is especially happy to see him. Here she is.

Did you spot everything?

Juggling balls

Useful equipment

Cecil the ghost

The chart below shows you how many juggling balls are hidden on each double page. You can also find out which piece of Sophie's useful equipment is hidden where.

Pages	Juggling balls	Useful equipment
4-5	one	none here!
6-7	four	monster protection shield
8-9	one	key
10-11	three	useful string
12-13	four	run-faster shoes
14-15	two	umbrella
16-17	three	monster phrase book
18-19	five	extra-brave toffees
20-21	two	monster protection helmet
22-23	three (or is it six?)	mystery box
24-25	four	powerful flashlight
26-27	one	none here!
28-29	nineteen	none here!

Did you remember to look out for Cecil the ghost? He is hiding spookily on every double page. Look back through the book again and see if you can find him.

Four friends

Now Sophie, Titus, Dennis and Princess Posy are very good friends. Every Saturday when the sun is shining, they play on the hill beside Puzzle Castle. If it's raining, they eat toast and cakes in Posy's room, and Jester Jim teaches them how to juggle. And because he has three new friends to play with, Dennis isn't afraid of Boris the Bad any more.

PUZZLE PLANET

Contents

About this story

This story is about a young astronaut called Archie, his robot Blip, and their adventures on Puzzle Planet. There is a puzzle on every double page. See if you can solve them all. If you get stuck, you can look at the answers on pages 63 and 64.

Space School Report
NAME: Archie

SUBJECT	GRADE
STAR SPOTTING	A+
ROCKET FLYING	A+
MOON WALKING	A+

Comment:
Archie is a very helpful member of class.

Archie

Blip

Archie's space base

Archie's school report

Archie is a junior astronaut who goes to space school. One day, in the summer, he gets a surprise letter. It is from the wisest astronaut teacher of them all, Professor Moon. Here is the letter.

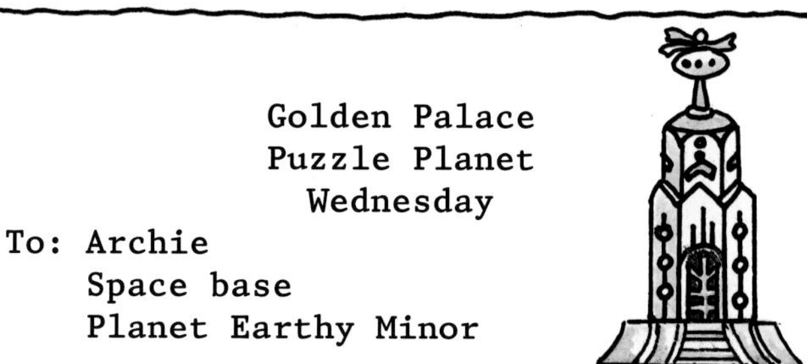

Golden Palace
Puzzle Planet
Wednesday

To: Archie
Space base
Planet Earthy Minor

Dear Archie,

I have read your space school report. Well done! Now you and some of your school friends have the chance to prove your skills as astronauts. You must travel to Puzzle Planet and find me in my Golden Palace by 4 o'clock on Thursday. If you succeed, I will award you with a special space badge which I only give to the bravest young astronauts in the universe.

From Professor Moon

P.S. I will send you a kit list of the things you need to bring to Puzzle Planet.

Things to spot

All good astronauts are observant. As soon as Archie arrives on Puzzle Planet, he must prove he is a good astronaut by spotting some special objects. These objects can only be found on Puzzle Planet. There is one hiding on each double page, from the moment Archie lands. Here they are.

Sneaky Sydney

Sydney lives on Puzzle Planet. He's a bit of a bully and likes spoiling people's games. Look out for Sydney's spy satellite. It's watching Archie on every double page.

Space newts

Puzzle Planet is the home of the pink space newts. There is at least one newt hiding on every double page, from the time Archie lands on Puzzle Planet. Look out for them!

Getting ready

Archie was looking forward to his very first visit to Puzzle Planet. Outside, his rocket was parked and was nearly ready for take off.

Archie looked at the kit list Professor Moon had sent him. It showed six useful things he would need to take to Puzzle Planet. Archie looked around his small space base in dismay. It was such a mess, how would he ever find the six things on the list?

Can you find the six things Archie needs?

KIT-LIST

Bring these things with you to Puzzle Planet. From Professor Moon.

tracker beam – for contacting other astronauts when in trouble (makes a beeping noise)

Puzzle Planet guide book

one space-buggy (exactly like this one)

one cosmic compass (exactly like this one)

bionic binoculars (exactly like these)

list of school friends going to Puzzle Planet to collect their special space badges

CONTROLS
UP
DOWN
UP LEVER
IN
OUT
RADIO
ASTRO LUNCH BOX
ARCHIE'S FILE

Star maze

Soon everything was ready for the journey. Now Archie had to plan his route to Puzzle Planet. He peered through his super-powerful telescope. Far, far away, he could see the red glow of Puzzle Planet.

In his little space base, Archie shivered and wondered if he would ever find a path through the twisty maze of stars shining in the galaxy.

Can you help Archie find a way through the star maze to Puzzle Planet?

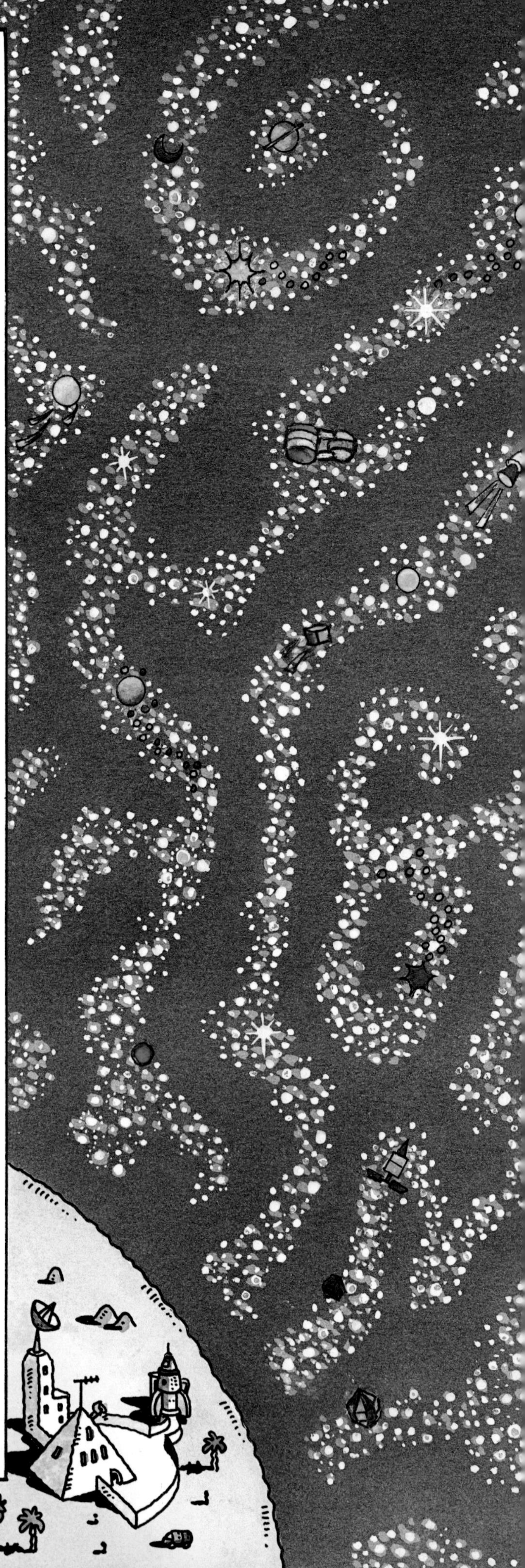

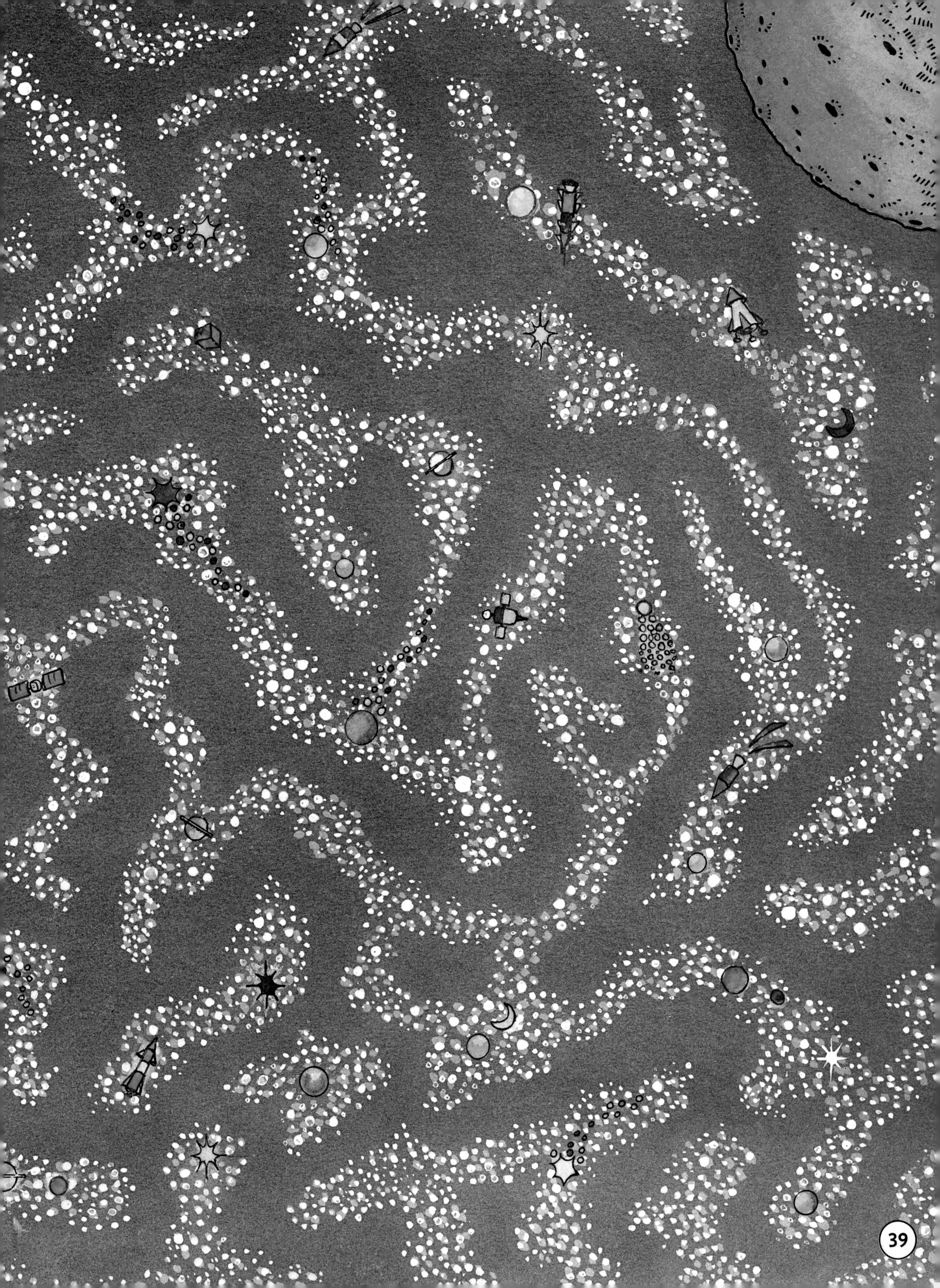

Space journey

At last it was time to set off. Archie made some final flight checks, took his travel-sickness pill and called to Blip. The two friends climbed aboard the space rocket. They closed the outer doors, fastened their seat belts and set the controls for Puzzle Planet.

Archie began the countdown. "5...4...3...2...1..."

Don't forget to look out for the special Puzzle Planet objects, Archie.

Remember to look out for us!

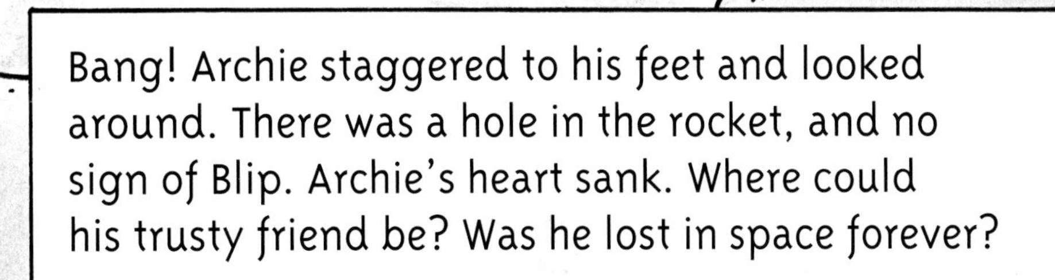

Bang! Archie staggered to his feet and looked around. There was a hole in the rocket, and no sign of Blip. Archie's heart sank. Where could his trusty friend be? Was he lost in space forever?

Can you find Blip?

Planet puzzle

Archie was very pleased to see Blip again. Now they had to find out exactly where they were on Puzzle Planet.

Archie spun his cosmic compass and walked a little way north into a small clearing. There were lots of strange things to look at. Archie got out his Puzzle Planet guide book and turned to the page he needed. He looked at the pictures carefully. By matching the pictures with what he saw in front of him, he could find out where they were.

Where are they?

• WHERE ARE YOU? A scenic guide to Puzzle Planet •
You are in a FRIENDLY part of Puzzle Planet if you can see...
blue volcano
yellow
green
red
trees just likes these
green pool
You are in a NASTY part of Puzzle Planet if you can see...
blue volcano
red
green
yellow
trees just likes these
orange pool
You are in a NICE part of Puzzle Planet if you can see...
green volcano
red
yellow
green
trees just likes these
orange pool
You are in a WILD and SCARY part of Puzzle Planet if you can see...
blue volcano
yellow
green
red
trees just likes these
orange pool
You are in a JOLLY part of Puzzle Planet if you can see...
blue volcano
yellow
red
green
trees just likes these
orange pool

Archie in trouble

Archie gulped. They were in a wild and scary part of Puzzle Planet! Suddenly there was a buzzing noise behind them. Archie spun around. It came from the rocket wreck. Archie and Blip rushed over to investigate. The video screen was on and someone was sending a message. It was Sydney, the space school bully.

"Archie, my magnetic field made you crash. I have done the same to three of your two-eyed, two-eared space mates. You won't get your special badges from Professor Moon now. Tee hee."

The picture faded. Archie picked up the list of his school friends who were also on their way to Professor Moon's palace. Archie thought back to Sydney's words, and soon knew which three friends were in trouble, somewhere on Puzzle Planet.

Which of Archie's space friends are in trouble?

Ice storm

There was no time to lose. Archie had to find his friends. He switched on his tracker beam. If another astronaut was in trouble he'd soon find out. Sure enough, it began to beep. Archie pulled the space-buggy from the wreckage, put it into mega-drive, and zoomed off.

Within seconds they were speeding past strange snowy scenery. Suddenly a huge ball of ice fell from the sky.

"It's an ice-meteor storm!" Archie cried. "We must find shelter before it smashes us into pieces!"

Can you see a safe, empty cave where Archie, Blip and the buggy can find shelter?

Bubble trouble

The storm passed and they drove safely on. Ahead, on top of a small mountain, a rocket had crashed. Someone was in trouble! All of a sudden a big bubble floated past. Trapped inside was Pete from Planet Putty. Archie was about to burst the bubble when he saw another one, with another Pete inside, then another, and another.

"I bet this is Sydney's trick," thought Archie.
"Only one is the real Pete. The rest are slightly different."

Which is the real Pete?

You have seen a picture of Pete on page 45.

Spacey swamp

Pete jumped aboard the buggy and they bounced on. Soon they came to a stop at a slimy green swamp. In the middle was Betty from Blarg, trapped on top of her sinking rocket. They had to rescue her and reach the other side to continue their journey.

Pete was an expert on swamps. He knew that there was only one safe way to cross. They must step from one plant or creeper to the next. But they mustn't tread on anything with red spots. They would have to be very careful.

Can you rescue Betty and reach the other side?

Help, my foot is caught. I'm trapped!

Giant snails

Back on dry land, the friends saw a space ship surrounded by giant snails. Inside was a worried Victor the Vargon.

"These slimy creatures are hungry!" he cried.

"It's OK, Victor," yelled Betty. "The Puzzle Planet snails like eating blue space bananas best, and I can see seven, one for each of them!"

Can you find seven blue bananas?

Yum, yum.
Oh!
I'm glad I'm not a banana.

Following the signal

"Now let's find Professor Moon," said Archie, as the snails began to eat the blue bananas.

They were just wondering which way to go when Archie's tracker beam began to beep. Someone else was in trouble. The noise came from the end of the path ahead.

At the end was a small room, but there was no one in trouble here. Then Archie knew they had been tricked. There were things in this room he had seen before.

What things has Archie seen before?
Who do you think they belong to?

Trapped!

They were in Sydney's secret hide-out. In the room ahead stood Sydney himself.

"You walked straight into my trap," he smiled. "There's no escape. You won't find Professor Moon now."

Everyone was very scared, but Blip wasn't afraid. He looked at Sydney and his antenna began to twitch. He knew exactly how to make Sydney disappear and give the space friends time to escape.

What can the friends do to make Sydney disappear?

SYDNEY'S BEST TRICKS TO PLAY ON FRIENDS

BLACK HOLE – *friend sits in dark for ten mega-minutes*

GARBAGE CHUTE – *covers friend in galactic garbage*

TRAP NET – *friend caught inside for six mega-minutes*

TELEPORTER – *sends friend to an unknown destination for one mega-hour*

GARBAGE CHUTE
BROKEN
PROF MOON
SYDNEY rules O.K
TRAP NET
Worn and Torn
TELEPORTER
The Mekons
COUSIN
Galaxie 500
THE METEORS
WAY OUT
INTASTELLA
Special Shoes
LIGHT
DO NOT TOUCH
STOP
BLUE SWITCH
1
2
3
OFF
ON
BEEP
ZING
BLOOP
GO
A
B
ZOOM
ZAP
bubbles
TELEPORTER SWITCH
ZIP
ZOP
Star Switch
HOT CHOC.
Spare Socks
LOLLIES

Canyon maze

Blip flicked the teleporter switch on and Sydney vanished. The friends dived through the door on the other side of the room, pausing to grab some useful skateboards. They skated down a chute and skidded to a stop at the edge of a maze of canyons. In the distance they could see three gold buildings.

"One of those is Professor Moon's palace!" cried Betty. "I recognize it from his letter. We'll skate there in no time."

Which is Professor Moon's palace?
Can you find a way to it?

Just in time

Archie and his friends skated into the palace, just as the clock struck four. They saw lots of familiar faces, all smiling and cheering.

"If it wasn't for Archie, we wouldn't have made it to the palace at all," said Betty.

She told everyone about their adventures. Professor Moon gave Archie an extra award for being especially brave. Even Blip had a tasty treat. They were very proud and pleased.

Do you recognize everyone here?
Can you spot the unexpected guest?

WELCOME ASTRONAUTS
Well done!

Puzzle Planet creatures

Did you notice that there are some very strange creatures living on Puzzle Planet? Below is a page from Archie's guide book. It shows pictures of some of them.

You can also read about each creature. Whereabouts on Puzzle Planet do you think each one lives? Why not see if you can find them all?

YOU MIGHT SEE...

Angry Armadillo
This hard-shelled creature will nip an astronaut's ankle.

Yellow Billed Bird
Likes to dribble swamp water onto strangers.

Cave Dog
Lives in dark places and enjoys chewing robots.

Galactic Geek
Likes to sharpen its teeth on space buggies.

Ice Bird
Its feathers are as cold as snow. It has an icicle tail.

Plunger Nose
Harmless, unless it sniffs you, and then – watch out!

Beardy Bird
This friendly bird likes having splashy mud baths.

Mushroom Bird
If you touch the red spotted ones, you'll get an itchy rash.

Swamp Serpent
One will suck your socks, the other will chew your toes.

Answers

Pages 36-37 Getting ready
The six things Archie must take to Puzzle Planet are circled in red.

Pages 38-39 Star maze
The way through the star maze to Puzzle Planet is shown in red.

Pages 40-41 Space journey
Blip is here.

Pages 42-43 Planet puzzle
Archie has landed in a wild and scary part of Puzzle Planet.

Pages 44-45 Archie in trouble
The three friends in trouble are:

Betty from Blarg

Victor the Vargon

Pete from Planet Putty

Pages 46-47 Ice storm
Archie, Blip and the buggy can take shelter in this safe and empty cave.

Pages 48-49 Bubble trouble
This is the real Pete.

Pages 50-51 Spacey swamp
The route to Betty, and then to the other side of the swamp is shown in red.

Pages 52-53 Giant snails
The seven blue bananas are circled in red.

Pages 54-55 Following the signal
Archie has seen these switches and this microphone on page 44. They belong to Sydney.

Pages 56-57 Trapped!
Sydney is standing on the teleporter. Blip switches the teleporter on. Sydney disappears to an unknown destination!

Pages 58-59 Canyon maze
This is Professor Moon's palace. The way to it is shown in red.

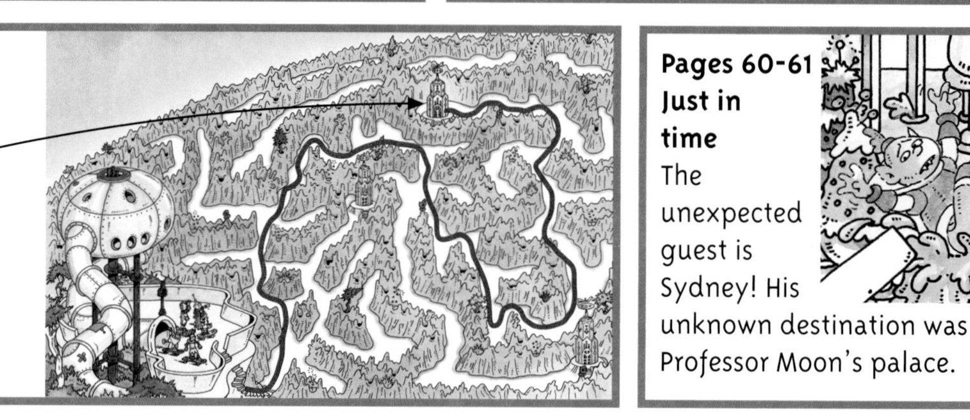

Pages 60-61 Just in time
The unexpected guest is Sydney! His unknown destination was Professor Moon's palace.

Did you spot everything?

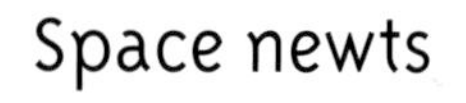

Space newts

Things to spot

Spy satellite

Remember that Archie must spot certain things once he arrives on Puzzle Planet. The chart below shows you how many space newts are hiding on each double page. You can also find out which of the Puzzle Planet objects is hidden where.

Did you remember to watch out for Sydney's spy satellite? Look back through the book and see if you can spot the satellite on each double page.

Pages	Space newts	Things to spot
40-41	three	star plant
42-43	three	bread fruit tree
44-45	two	green spider
46-47	one	footprint
48-49	five	Puzzle Planet flag
50-51	three	scaley goldfish
52-53	three	giant pink marshmallow
54-55	three	Puzzle Planet pencil
56-57	one	Puzzle Planet bug
58-59	one	red rock
60-61	five	friendly toffee apple

What happened next?
Although Sydney played some rather sneaky tricks on Archie and his friends, he did make it to Professor Moon's palace in the end. In fact, he was very well-behaved, and only had three helpings of Puzzle pop. Maybe next year it will be Sydney's turn to get his special badge, and be a real astronaut as well. What do you think?

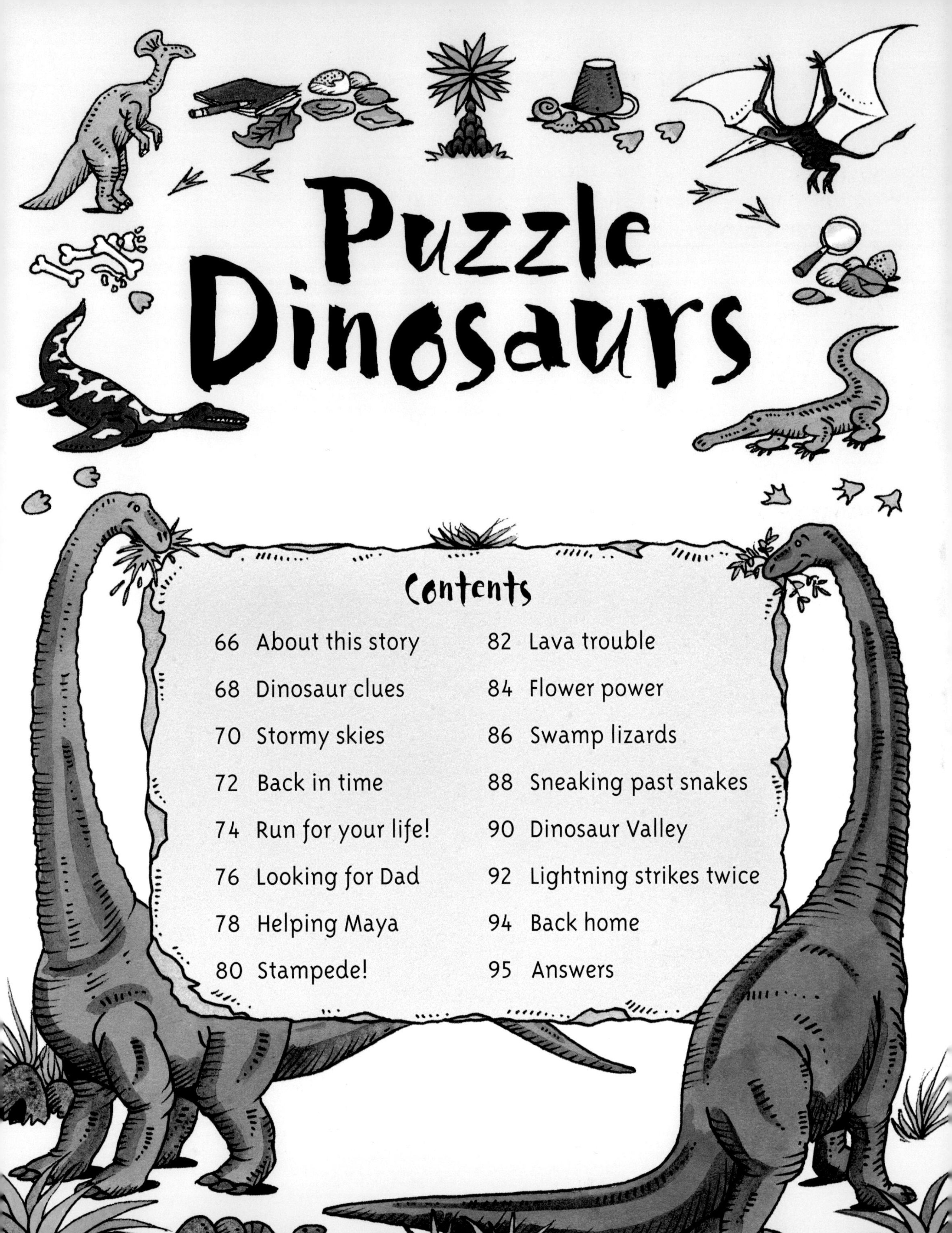

Puzzle Dinosaurs

Contents

About this story

This story is about Abby and Isaac and their amazing dinosaur discovery. There are puzzles to solve on every double page. If you get stuck, you can look at the answers on pages 95 and 96.

Abby and Isaac are staying by the sea. A fierce storm has washed up lots of interesting things onto the beach, and Abby and Isaac investigate.

They spot a big rock, imprinted with a strange creature. Isaac is sure they have found a fossil. Excitedly, he takes a photo with his new camera.

Things to spot

Abby and Isaac don't know it yet, but they are about to go on an amazing dinosaur adventure. See if you can spot one of these prehistoric things on every double page.

Dinosaur teeth

Look out for dinosaur teeth. There is one tooth to spot on every double page.

Morgan the Morganacudon

This prehistoric creature is a Morganacudon. His name is Morgan. See if you can spot him on every double page.

Dinosaur clues

That night, Abby and Isaac lay listening to the sound of the waves crashing onto the shore. Another storm was brewing. Outside, the moon cast its light over the fossil on the beach.

Abby took a closer look at the photo Isaac had taken earlier.

"I'm sure this is a dinosaur fossil," she said. "It has a long, pointy tail and short front legs. Is there anything like that in your dinosaur book, Isaac?"

Can you help Isaac identify the fossilized dinosaur?

Dinosaurs from the late Cretaceous period.

MEAT EATERS

Troodon: Long tailed. Liked to eat Maiasaurus!

T Rex: Big and bad. The daddy of the dinosaurs!

Deinonychus: This dinosaur was built to kill!

PLANT EATERS

Edmontosaurus: A large duck-billed dinosaur.

Achelousaurus: A plant eater with a parrot-like beak.

Maiasaura: It had a long, pointy tail and back legs bigger than its front legs.

Parasaurolophus: Plant eater with a pointy tail.

www.usborne.com
Deadly bees lived in these beehives
A prehistoric poisonous snake

Stormy skies

Just then, a flash of lightning struck the fossil and a blinding light filled the room. When the light faded, Isaac and Abby found themselves back on the beach. The tide was rolling in. On a rock in the middle of the deep water was a familiar-looking creature.

"It's a dinosaur!" Isaac cried. "A Maiasaura, just like the fossil we found. Except this one's alive."

"And stranded on that rock," Abby pointed. "I think I can see a way to lead it to safety before the tide comes in."

Can you find a safe way across the sandbanks and rocks to reach the little dinosaur?

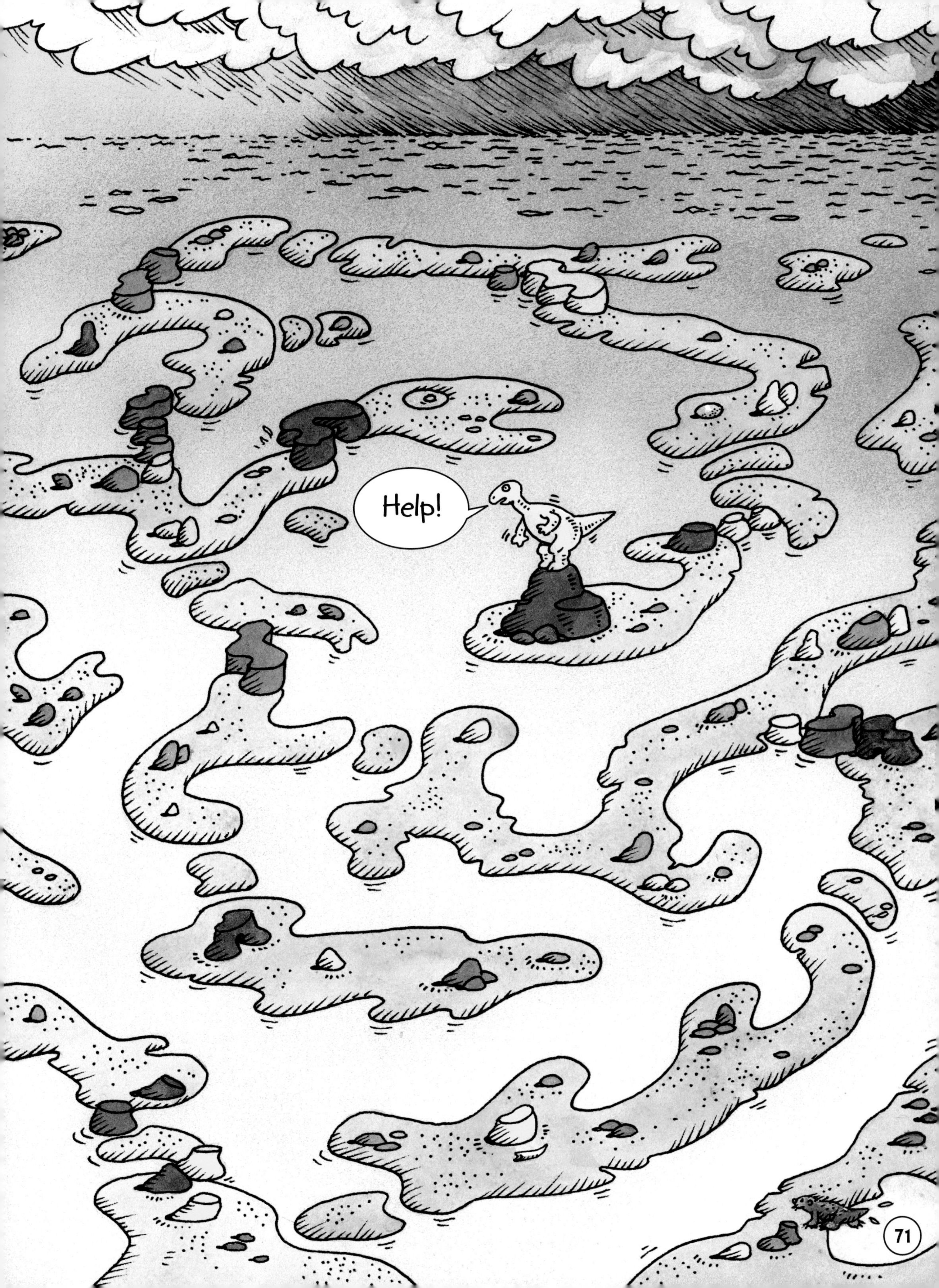

Help!

Back in time

Isaac and Abby scrambled safely across to the Maiasaura. The dinosaur looked surprised to see them, but the children were even more surprised when it actually spoke to them.

"I've lost my parents and I'm stuck on this rock!" it wailed.

"Don't worry," Abby said kindly as they led the dinosaur to the safety of the shore. "We'll help you."

Isaac was trying to make sense of everything. "This Maiasaura must have come alive in our time," he said.

"Or else," he continued, spotting something very scary in the bushes. "We've somehow gone back to the time of the dinosaurs. Look out!"

What has Isaac spotted?

Run for your life!

Crashing through the trees came a terrifying, giant dinosaur.

"It's a meat eater!" cried Maya. "Run for your lives!"

Isaac and Abby didn't need to be told twice. One blast of hot breath from the prehistoric monster was enough to make them sprint for cover.

...and climbed up. The meat eater shook the tree with his mighty claws. Isaac thought he would fall. Then, just when he thought things couldn't get any worse, he saw another type of meat-eating dinosaur – and then some more.

Can you spot the other five meat-eating dinosaurs?

Looking for Dad

Isaac closed his eyes. He thought this was it. Then he heard Abby shout, "Quick, climb down."

Isaac opened his eyes. The meat eaters were all attacking each other! Isaac grabbed his chance and raced down to join Abby and Maya in the bushes.

"Let's get out of here before they spot us again," whispered Abby.

This is your print, Maya.

The trio ran quickly. They came to a clearing. Here, lots of strange tracks led off in different directions in the ground.

"Some of these look like your paw prints, only bigger," Abby said to Maya.

"They might be my parents' prints," Maya said excitedly. "My dad's are easy to spot. He's missing part of a toe. He lost it in a fight."

Can you spot Maya's dad's prints here?

Helping Maya

As the ground became drier, the prints stopped. Then, Isaac spotted them again in the muddy earth on the other side of a mountainous maze.

"Should we go any further?" Abby whispered to Isaac. "How will we get home again?"

"I don't know," he replied. "But we can't leave Maya here by herself."

"Yes, you're right," said Abby. "We should find her parents. Let's go."

"Hey, wait," Isaac said. "I think those long-necked creatures are Ornithomimus. They can be fierce and fast when they're awake."

"Those long-nosed things are nasty too," added Maya. "We'd better step carefully and quietly."

Can you find a safe way to the prints, avoiding the Ornithomimus, and the long-nosed creatures?

Stampede!

Safely through the twisty maze, Maya soon spotted her dad's prints again. They set off on the trail.

"Um, what's that noise?" Isaac said, hearing a faint drumming sound. "It's getting closer."

"Dinosaurs!" cried Abby.

A herd of stampeding dinosaurs raced towards them, trampling everything in their path. It was time to get out of the way – and fast.

Can you find them a safe, empty hiding place from the stampeding dinosaurs? Do you know what type of dinosaurs these are?

Lava trouble

Maya peered out from their hiding place.
"All the creatures I can see here are friendly," she said. "They were just stampeding because they were scared. And I know why. Look!" She pointed to an erupting volcano, noisily spouting out fire and ash.

"The friendly creatures are hiding now," said Maya.

"Is it safe to go out?" asked Abby.

"Not yet," Isaac warned. "I can see a rather frightening creature. And what's more, I think it can fly."

What has Isaac seen? Where have the friendly creatures hidden?

Flower power

Isaac pointed up at the sky. A group of mean-eyed flying reptiles came screeching overhead, their pointed beaks poised to attack.

Isaac drew back his outstretched arm, but it was too late. One of the flapping monsters had scratched him on the arm with its razor-sharp claws.

"I think we lost them," Abby panted. "How's your arm, Isaac?"

Isaac looked miserable. "Badly scratched," he said.

Maya took a look. "Don't worry. I know a beautiful orange flower with pink leaves that will soothe that," she said.

"I can see it!" said Abby.

Can you spot the soothing orange flower?

Swamp lizards

Isaac rubbed his arm with the soothing leaves.

"That's much better," he smiled.

"At least it's cooler away from that volcano," said Abby.

They rounded a corner and found they were staring at an enormous swamp.

"I can see my dad's prints on the other side," exclaimed Maya. "We have to get across, but we'd better be careful. Dangerous giant lizards live in this swamp."

Isaac spotted a fallen tree trunk and Abby grabbed some branches. "We can paddle across on this log," they grinned. "Come on!"

Can you find a safe way through the swamp? Look out for the giant lizards!

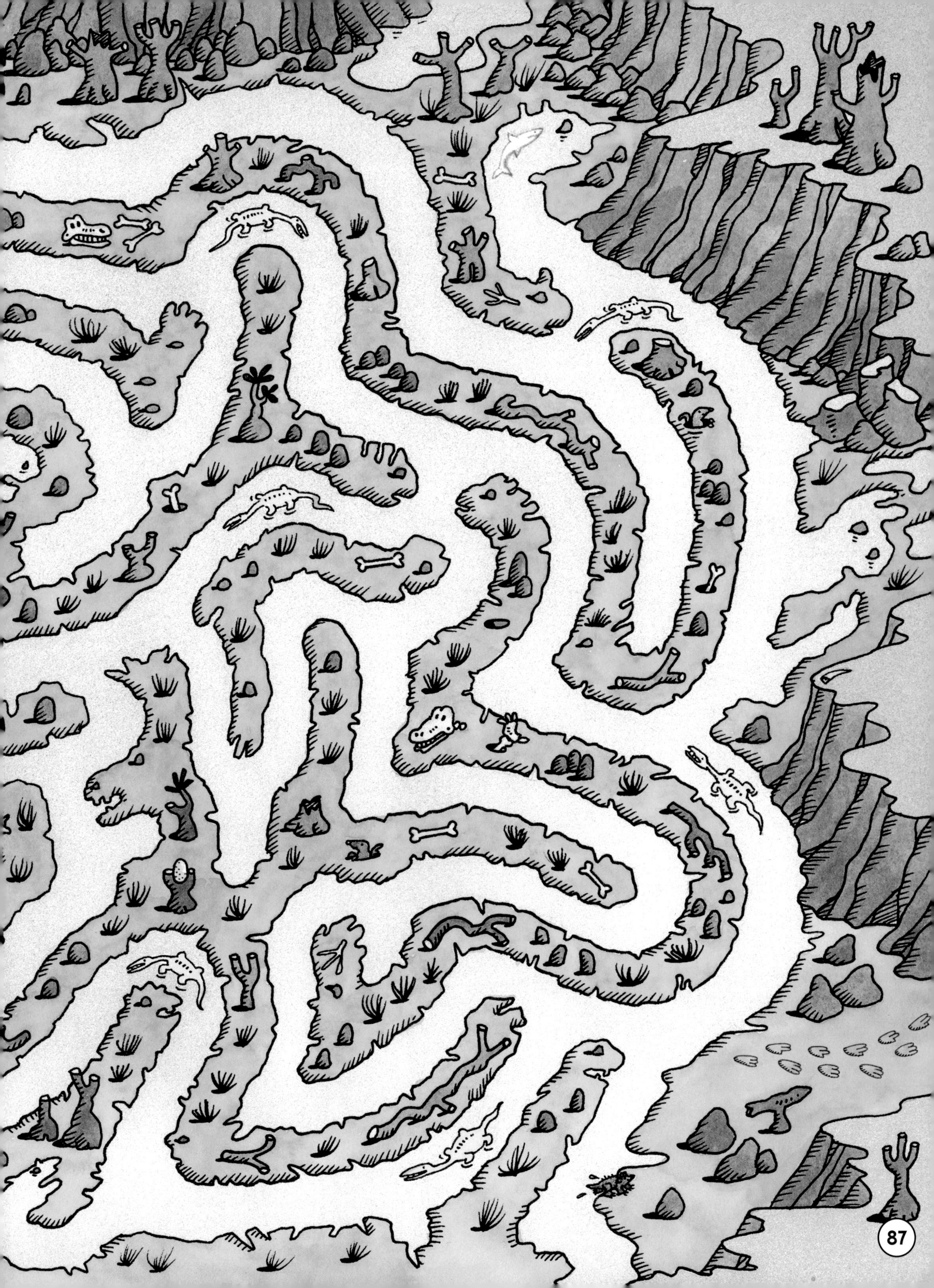

Sneaking past snakes

They jumped off the log, ran down a path and bumped straight into a huge dinosaur. Isaac was about to turn and flee, when Maya let out an excited yell.

"It's my friend, Al."

"Maya," Al whispered. "Where have you been? We've all been worried. And what are those strange creatures with you?"

"They're not strange," Maya said. "They're Abby and Isaac. I was lost and they rescued me. Why are we whispering, Al?"

"Because the trees here are full of poisonous snakes," hissed Al. "There are deadly beehives too. Climb onto my back. I'll sneak quietly past and take you to your parents. But you will have to help me look out for the dangerous creatures."

Can you spot the snakes? There are ten of them. There are four deadly beehives too.

Dinosaur Valley

Quietly and carefully, Al crept off into the jungle, away from the snakes. Then, around a corner was the most amazing sight. A mighty herd of dinosaurs grazed by a lake. Isaac thought he recognized some of them from his dinosaur book.

Suddenly Maya gave a cry of excitement. "My parents!"

Can you spot Maya's parents? How many other types of dinosaur do you think Isaac can recognize?

Lightning strikes twice

Maya's parents were overjoyed to see her. "We heard the meat eaters coming and we called to you to run," her dad explained. "But you had wandered away from us, Maya and we couldn't find you. We thought we'd never see you again."

"I'm safe now, thanks to my new friends Abby and Isaac," Maya smiled.

As they talked, dark clouds appeared overhead and the wind began to blow. A flash of lightning filled the sky, and in that moment the dinosaurs disappeared. Abby and Isaac found themselves back in the beach house. Isaac's dinosaur book was still on the bed. The fossil was still outside the window. Or was it?

What has happened to the fossil?

Back home

The next morning, Abby and Isaac were back on the beach, but they couldn't stop thinking about their amazing dinosaur adventure.

"Maya isn't a fossil anymore," Isaac said, looking at the empty stone. "So I guess when we went back in time, we must have saved her life."

"I'm glad she's with her parents again," Abby sighed. "But I'm going to miss her."

"Me too," agreed Isaac. He reached into his bag for his camera, to take a picture of the space where Maya had been. "Hey, I almost forgot," he said, pulling out something round. "I picked up this interesting rock on our adventure. Look."

"Isaac, that isn't a rock. It's a dinosaur egg!" Abby cried. "And I think it's about to hatch!"

Look back through the story. Can you spot a dinosaur egg on each double page?

Answers

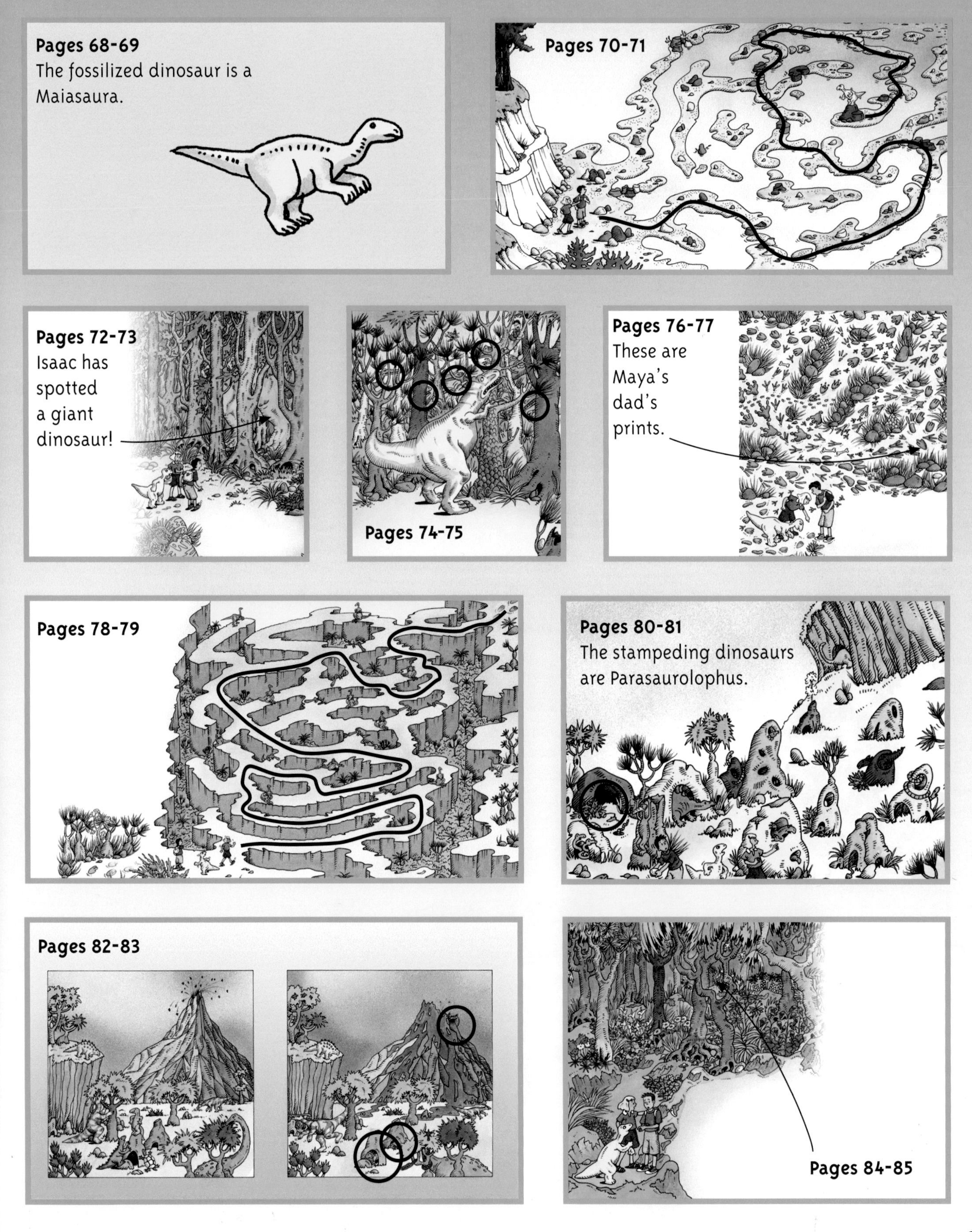

Pages 68-69
The fossilized dinosaur is a Maiasaura.
Pages 70-71
Pages 72-73
Isaac has spotted a giant dinosaur!
Pages 74-75
Pages 76-77
These are Maya's dad's prints.
Pages 78-79
Pages 80-81
The stampeding dinosaurs are Parasaurolophus.
Pages 82-83
Pages 84-85

pages 86-87

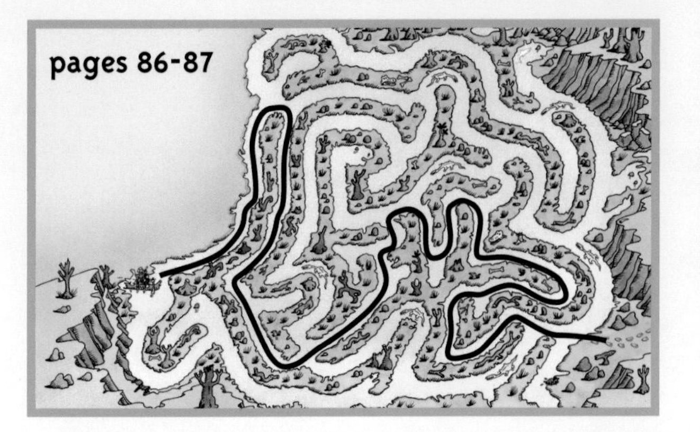

Pages 88-89

Pages 90-91
Here are Maya's parents. Some of the other dinosaurs here are Parasaurolophus, Achelousaurus, Edmontosaurus. (You saw them in Isaac's dinosaur book on page 68.)

Pages 92-93
The stone is empty and the fossilized Maya has disappeared.

Page 94

Did you spot the dinosaur eggs? (There isn't one on pages 66 and 67.)

Did you spot everything?

Did you spot Morgan the Morganacudon on every double page?

And did you find the dinosaur teeth?

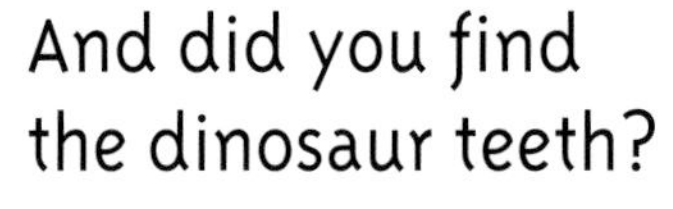

What next?
In the next story, you'll go on an exciting adventure around Puzzle Holiday Park. Can you score enough points to become a Super Supreme Spotter?

The list shows you where the things to spot are hidden.

pages	objects
68-69	amber
70-71	ammonite
72-73	big blue rat
74-75	flying frog
76-77	newt
78-79	gingko tree
80-81	tortoise
82-83	star-tailed snake
84-85	dragonfly
86-87	ghost shark
88-89	Stegoceras
90-91	prehistoric sea otter
92-93	blue claw

PUZZLE HOLIDAY

Contents

About this story

This story is about Katy and Tim and their trip to the Puzzle Holiday Park. Katy and Tim love puzzles. There is one for them to solve on every double page. Can you help them? If you get stuck you can look at the answers on pages 127 and 128.

Katy's and Tim's adventure began with an exciting package that landed on their doorstep. Inside was a letter from their friend Molly.

Molly

Dear Katy and Tim,

I've got a fantastic new job at the Puzzle Holiday Park. Come and stay with me for the weekend.

Catch the red and yellow Holiday Express bus from the town square at ten o'clock on Saturday morning. See you soon!

Love

Molly

P.S. Special Holiday Hats are enclosed. Please wear them at all times.

Holiday Hat

Stinky skunks

There is at least one stinky skunk hiding on every double page from pages 102-103. Look out for them, but hold your nose!

Supreme Spotters' Challenge

There are all kinds of weird and wonderful things to see in and around the Puzzle Holiday Park. You will find them all listed below. There is something to spot on every double page. Collect the points as you go and add up your score at the end of your adventure to find out how you did.

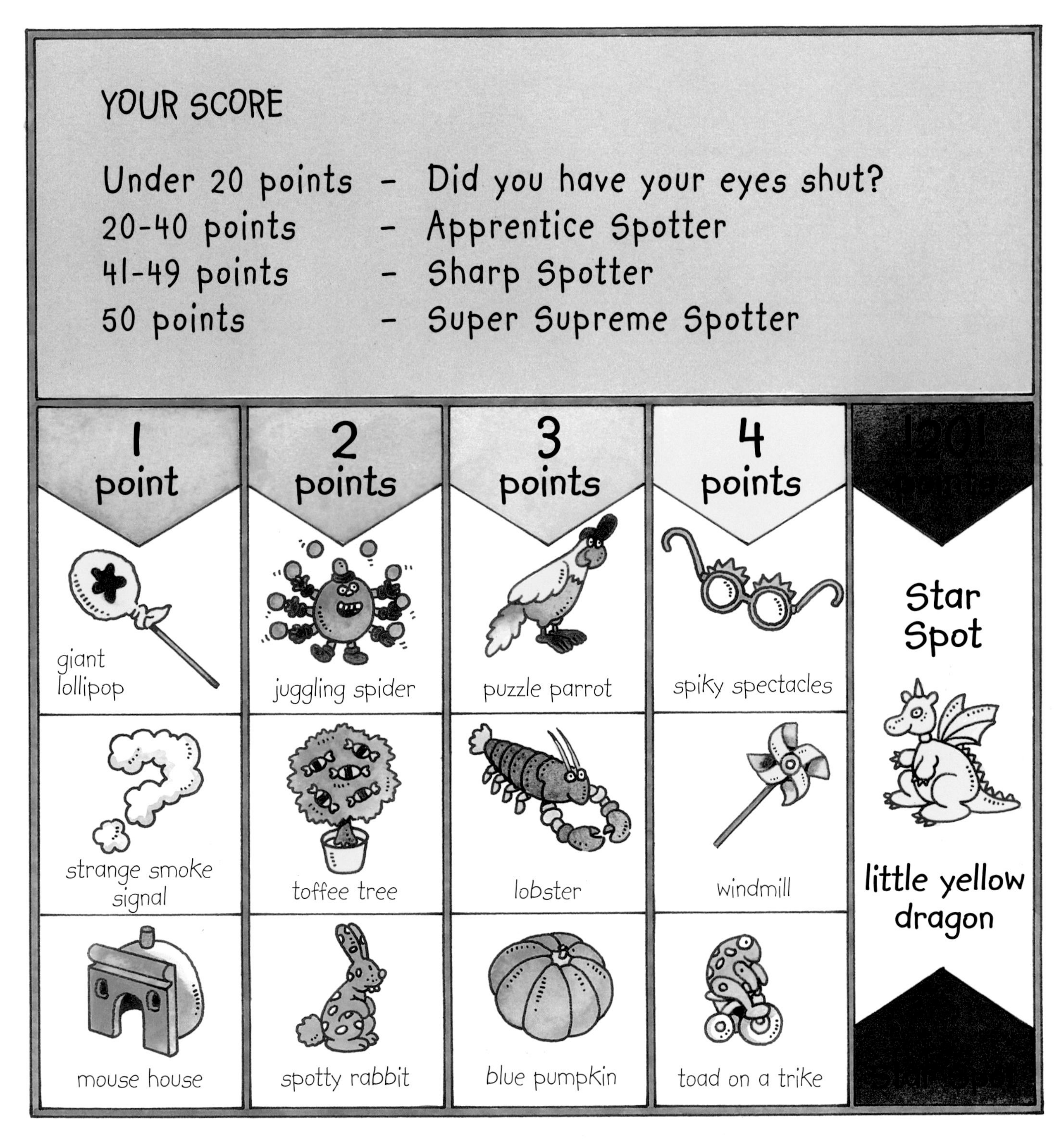

Puzzle Holiday!

On Saturday morning at ten o'clock, Katy and Tim stood in the town square. They were very excited to be going to the Puzzle Holiday Park.

Katy and Tim wore their special Holiday Hats and looked around eagerly for the red and yellow Holiday Express bus.

"I can see an elephant in a truck and a monkey driving a car," said Tim.

"And there's a camper van with lots of luggage on the top," said Katy. "But where's our bus?"

Can you help Katy and Tim find the Holiday Express bus?

built 1903
PUZZLE LIBRARY
PUZZLE POOL
Candy Store
Learn to SWIM!
PUZZLE CAFE
All aboard PUZZLE TRAIN!
Come to PUZZLE HOLIDAY PARK!

On the way

Katy and Tim climbed on board the Holiday Express bus.

"We'll pick up the other passengers on the way," the driver called.

And soon they were leaving the town far behind and driving through the countryside.

"Are all these people coming to the Holiday Park?" Katy and Tim cried as they stopped at a crossroads.

"Only the ones wearing special Holiday Hats like yours," grinned the driver.

Can you see who is going to the Holiday Park?

Listen carefully

At last they arrived at the Holiday Park. Molly came to meet them.

"Welcome everybody!" she called. "Now listen very carefully. I'm going to divide you up into four different groups. Each group will take part in all kinds of exciting activities. Read these instructions, then meet me at the campsite."

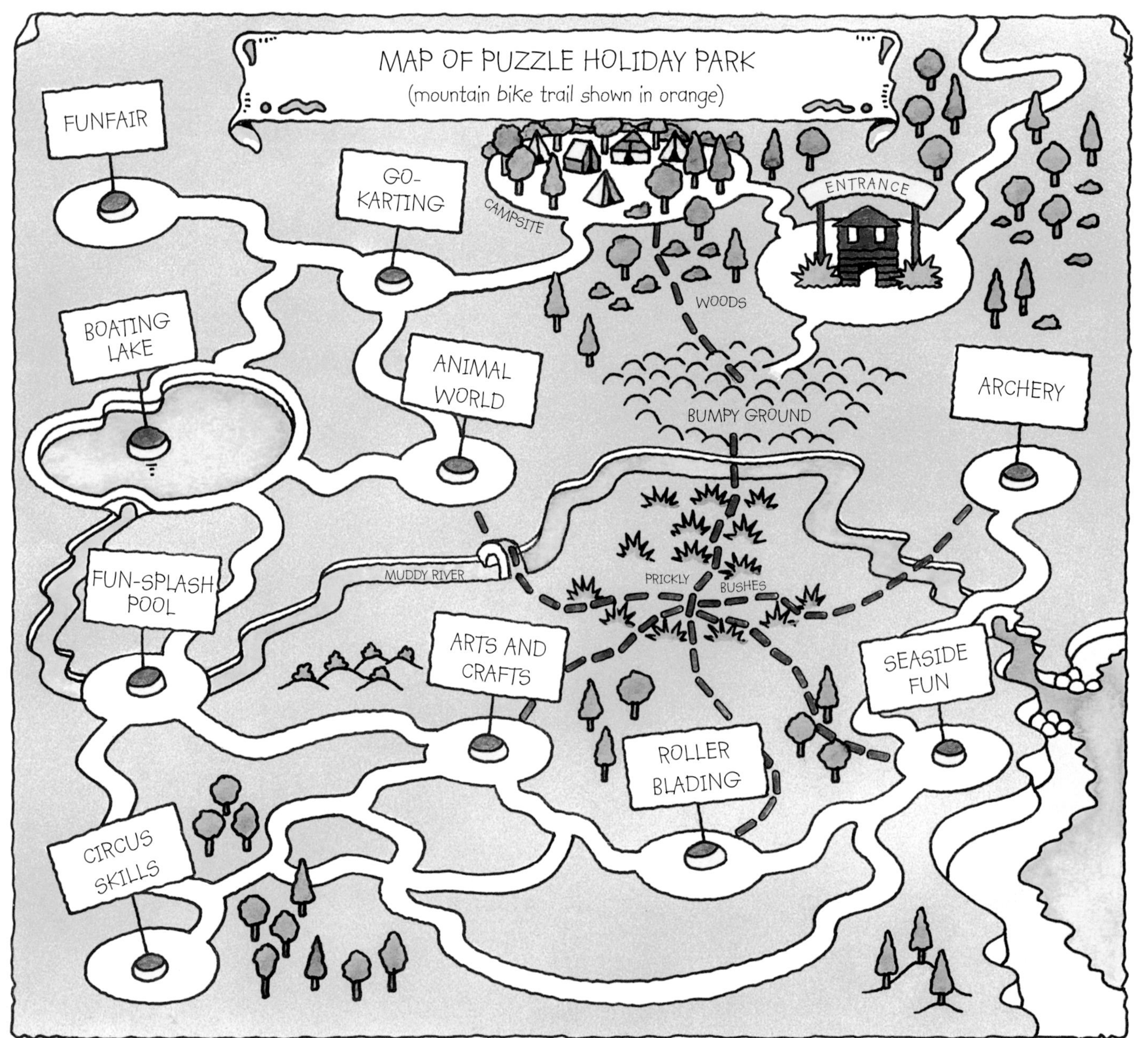

Then Molly gave them all timetables and a map of the Park. Katy and Tim looked for their names and saw what activities their group would be doing that day.

What group are Katy and Tim in?
What activities will they be doing and what route will they have to take?

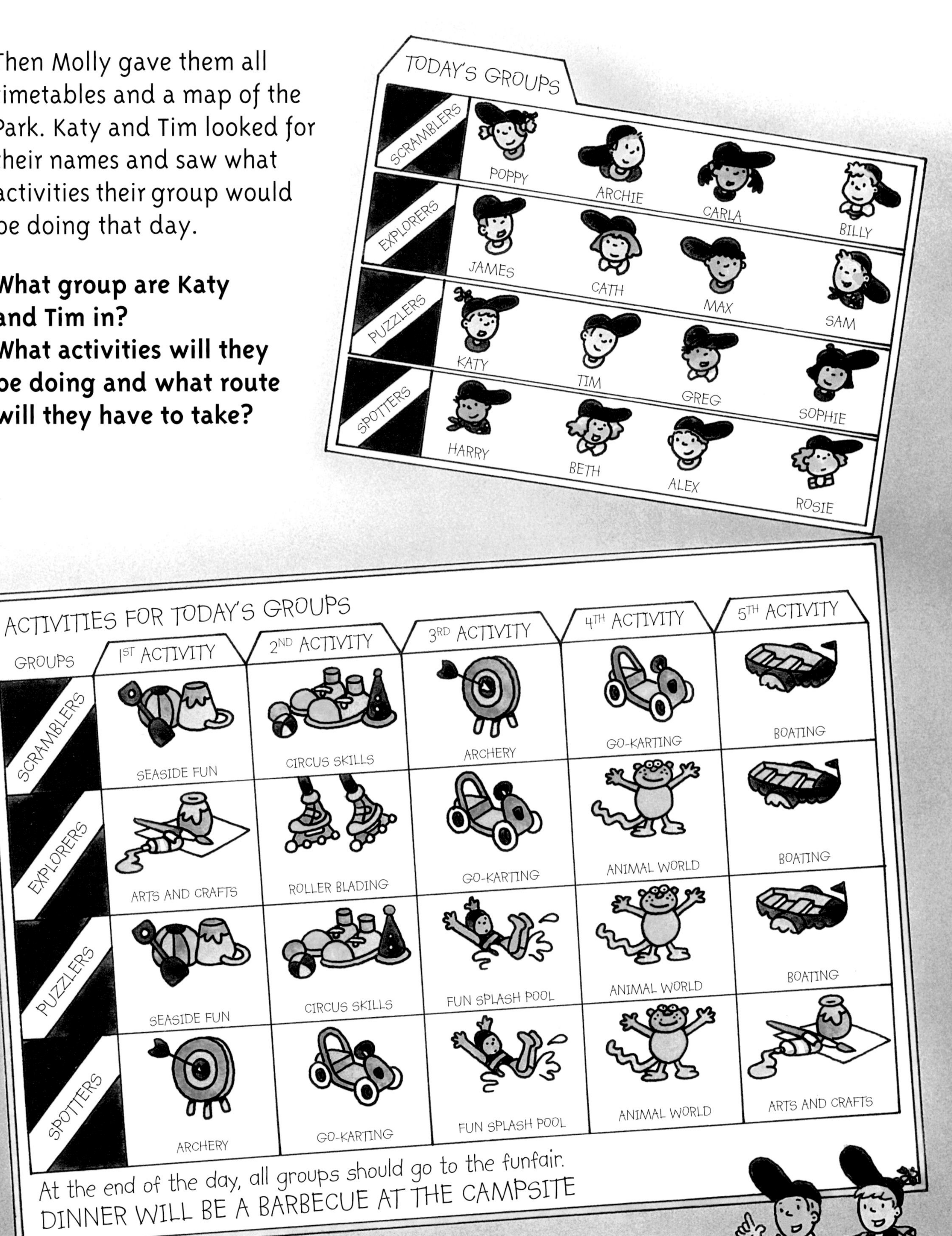

Tent trouble

Before the activities began, all the children went to the campsite. They saw tents and tepees, cabins and huts.

"Look at the pictures on the flags," Molly called. "Find the one that matches what you like doing best, and that's where you'll be sleeping tonight."

She turned away with a twinkle in her eye as everyone began to talk at once.

At last it was all figured out.

Listen to what everyone has to say. Can you see where they are all going to sleep?

Mountain bikes

When everyone had unpacked their bags, it was time for the fun to begin. Katy and Tim joined up with the other members of their group, Greg and Sophie. They looked at their timetable. Their first activity was at the seaside.

"You'll get there faster if you take the mountain bikes. Have fun," Molly said.

The Puzzlers grabbed their bikes.

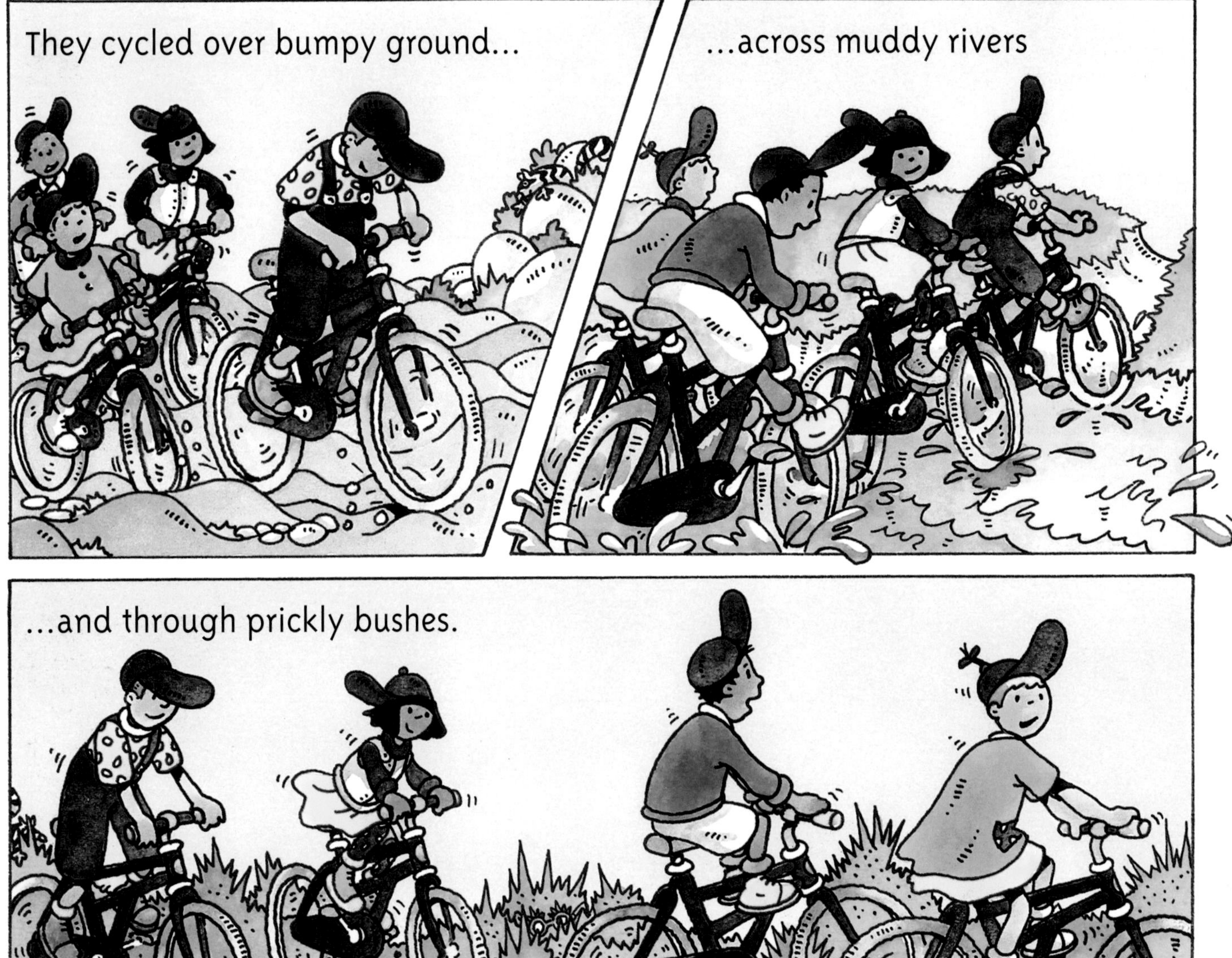

But then they stopped at a maze of paths. Which way should they go now? Other people were lost as well.

"Each path is scattered with clues!" Tim cried, looking at the ground. "It's easy to see where each one leads."

Can you find the paths everyone wants?

Seaside fun

The seaside was very busy. There were people everywhere! Katy and Tim and Sophie and Greg bounded onto the sand. They waved to the Scramblers.

"Come and build a sandcastle," called Beth, who was in charge of the beach. "It's a competition, but it isn't easy," she explained. "Each team's sandcastle has to include five blue pebbles, a feather, three red shells, some yellow seaweed and a flag. You've got half an hour to find everything on the beach. Go!"

Can you help find all the objects for both teams?

Half an hour later...
The sandcastles were finished. They were magnificent. But were they made with all the things that Beth had asked for?

Hillside scramble

The Puzzlers grinned, but the Scramblers groaned. They had left out one blue pebble.

"We'll beat you to the circus tent then," they cried as they raced off.

The Puzzlers raced after them, but the Scramblers had disappeared.

"There's the circus tent!" Greg pointed. "But we'll have to be careful how we get there. I can see some fallen rocks and log piles."

"And I've met some fearsome dragons before, but those wild animals look even scarier," Sophie shivered.

Can you find a safe way up the paths to the circus tent?

Yikes!

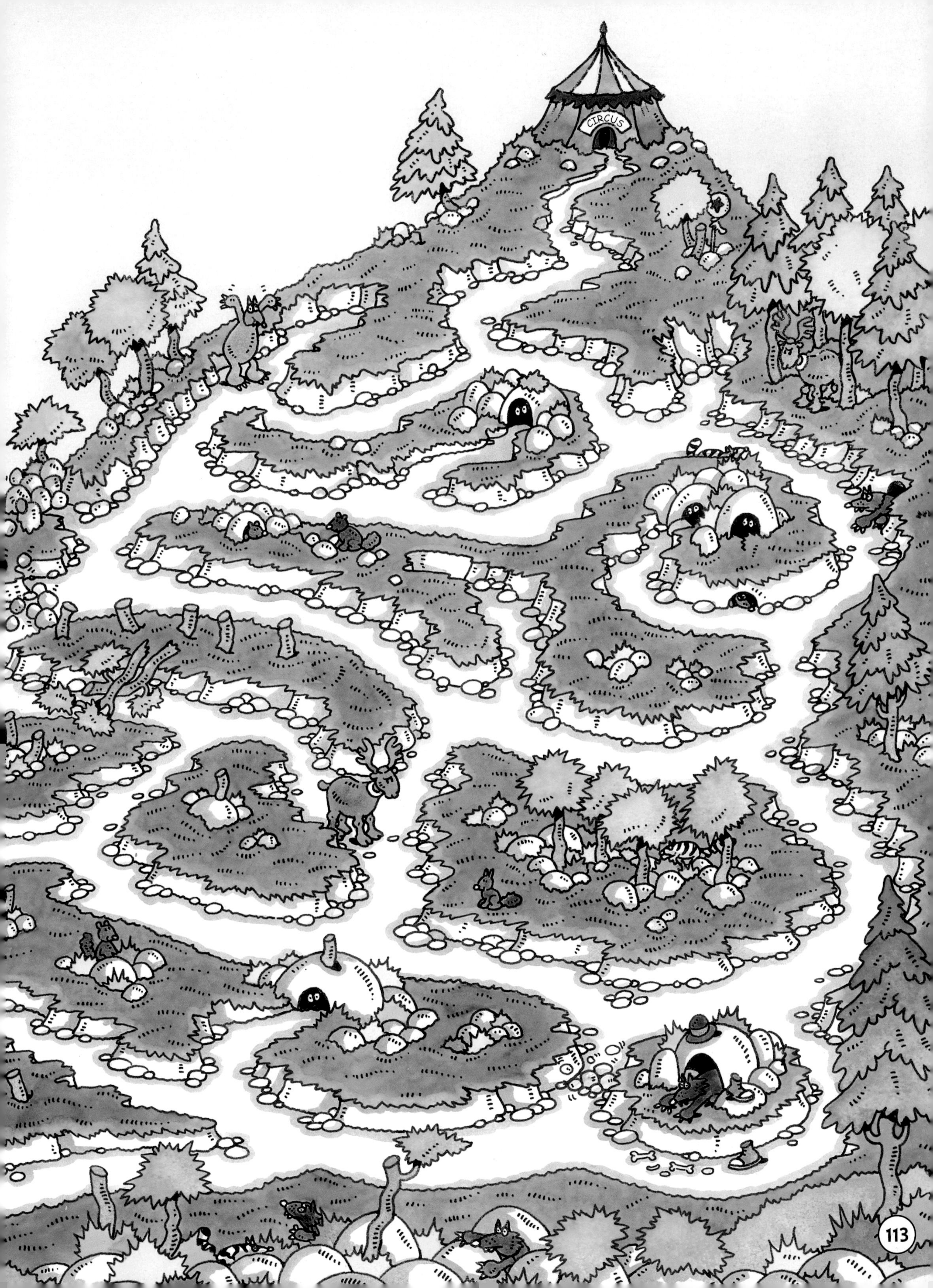
CIRCUS

Circus fun

Quickly the children climbed safely up the hill. When they reached the top, they peered inside the circus tent.

"Come in Puzzlers," cried a brightly dressed figure. "I'm Jester Jim and I'll be teaching you how to juggle today. You can have a ride on the unicycles too, or even try your hand at plate spinning."

Then one of the clowns fired a cannon. BOOM! There was a puff of smoke and, when it had cleared, things looked very different.

"Oh dear," wailed Jester Jim. "Everything's in a terrible muddle now. What's more, that loud noise made me drop all my juggling balls."

Can you spot all of the differences?

Water fun

When everything was straightened out, the children headed for their next treat – the Fun Splash Pool! They gasped at the sight of the water chutes. Quickly, they changed into their bathing suits.

"Watch me splash into the bubble pit!" Greg said.

"I hope I land in the Ball Pond!" Katy called.

"I want to end up in the Wavy Water," Tim cried.

"It's Castaway Cove for me," Sophie cheered.

Which slides must each of them take if they want to end up in these places?

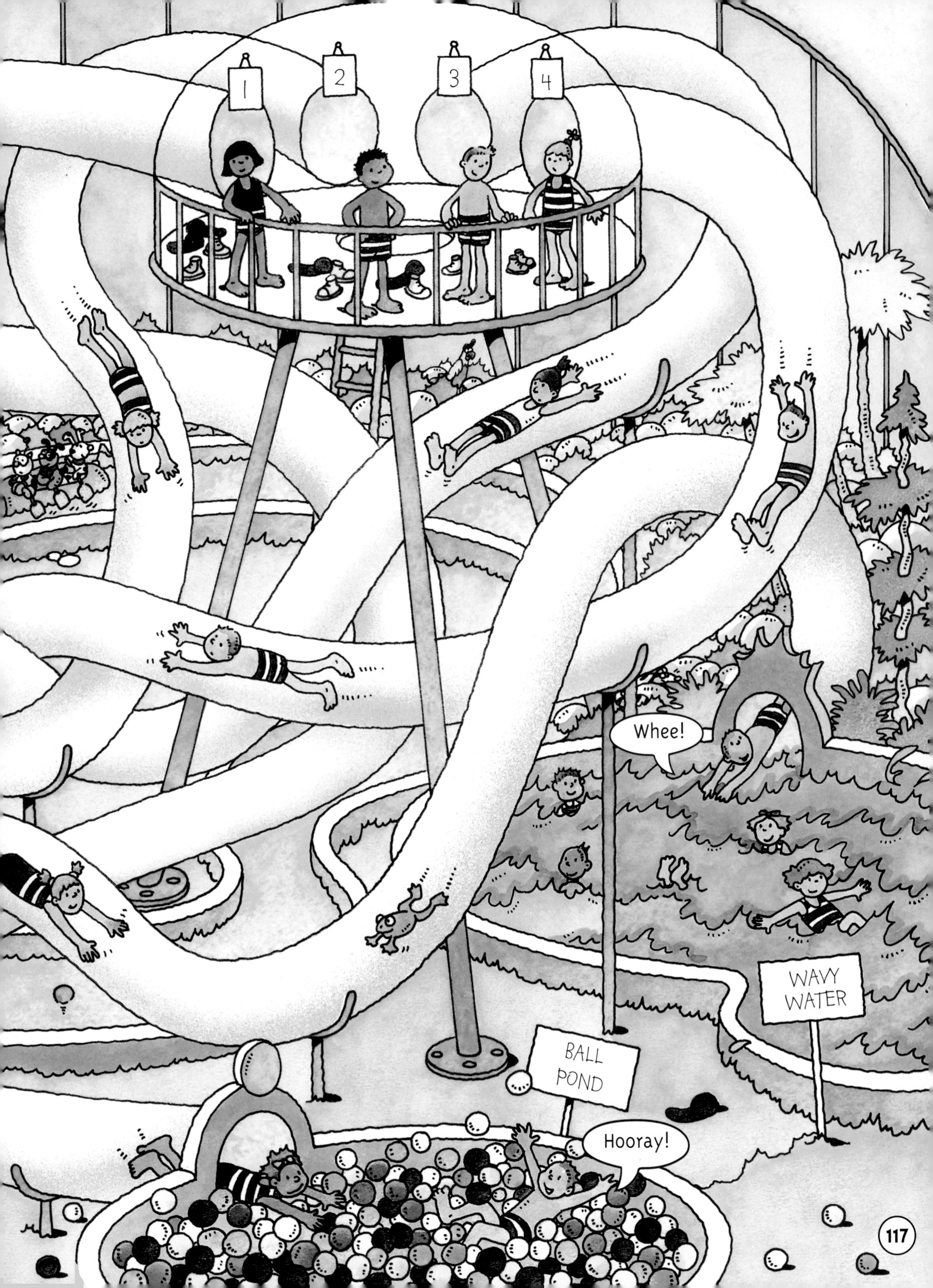
1
2
3
4
Whee!
WAVY WATER
BALL POND
Hooray!

Animal World

Shaking their wet hair, the Puzzlers packed up their swimming things and left the Fun Splash Pool.

"I could have stayed there all day," said Katy. "But we've got to get to Animal World."

But when they got there, they found the farmer, Tilly, shaking her head. All the animals were mooing and neighing and baaing and oinking and clucking and quacking and squawking.

"It's feeding time," Tilly called above the din. "Now where did I put the parrots' seed cakes and the monkeys' bananas? I can't find the bread for the ducks or the chickens' sack of corn. What about the basket of hay for the goats, and a milk bottle for each lamb?"

"Don't worry, we'll find the food," Katy called.

Can you help them?

Maa
Quack
CORN

Boating lake

The children left the animals gobbling up their food and headed for the Boating Lake. Boats of all shapes and sizes were out on the water.

"I knew we'd be late," said Katy, stopping to tie her shoelace. "Even the Explorers are here already."

"It's all right," said Sophie. "Some of the boats are being called in. Listen."

Can you spot the boats which are being called in?

Time's up for the red boat number 12,
the yellow boat number 28,
the green boat number 6 and
the blue and white boat number 37.
7
28
2
28
11
28
37
12
6
4
6
21
15
37
12
3

Fun at the fair

An hour later, the Puzzlers' boat was called in.

"I'm starving. When's dinner?" Tim wailed, looking at his timetable.

"Not yet," Katy smiled. "We haven't been to the funfair."

Quickly, they ran there. Everyone wanted to go on different rides...

"Look," Greg cried from the top of the wheel. "I can see our dinner cooking. It's time for the barbecue. Is everyone here?"

Are all the groups at the funfair?

Holiday feast

The children raced from the fairground to the barbecue. All kinds of delicious food was piled high. Tim's tummy rumbled.

"Hello everyone," Molly cried. "I hope you've had an exciting day. But before you start munching this lovely food, I have one more puzzle."

"Oh no," groaned Tim. "I'm starving!"

Molly smiled. "We've lost the toffee apples for dessert," she explained. "Can you find them all? There's one for all of you."

"Yum, yum," Tim cried. "That's one puzzle I don't mind solving!"

Can you find the toffee apples?

Starry night

That night, Katy and Tim lay snug in their tent and gazed up at the moon.

"What a wonderful time we've had," Katy sighed. "I don't think I've ever solved so many puzzles in one day."

"How did you do in the Supreme Spotters' Challenge?" Tim asked.

"I spotted everything," Katy said.

"So did I," said Tim. "That's 50 points."

"We're Super Supreme Spotters," Katy cried.

Are you?

Answers

Pages 100-101
Puzzle Holiday!
The Holiday Express bus is here.

Pages 102-103
On the way
The people circled here are going to the Puzzle Holiday Park.

Pages 104-105
Listen carefully
Katy and Tim are in the Puzzlers group. Their activities are seaside fun, circus skills, fun splash pool, animal world and the boating lake. At the end of the day, they will join up with everyone at the funfair. Their route is shown here.

Pages 106-107
Tent trouble
Match the letters to see who is sleeping in each tent.

Pages 108-109
Mountain bikes

This path leads to the archery.

This path leads to the seaside.

This path leads to the arts and crafts.

This path leads to the circus tent.

Pages 110-111
Seaside fun
The objects are circled below.

Pages 112-113
Hillside scramble
The safe way up the paths is shown here.

Pages 114-115
Circus fun
The differences are circled below.

Pages 116-117
Water fun

Greg must take slide 3.

Katy must take slide 1.

Tim must take slide 2.

Sophie must take slide 4.

Pages 118-119
Animal World
The animals' food is circled here.

Pages 120-121
Boating lake
The boats circled here are being called in.

Pages 122-123
Fun at the fair
Yes, all of the groups are here!
Look out for the red holiday hats.

Pages 124-125
Holiday feast
The toffee apples are circled here.

Did you spot everything?

Supreme Spotters' Challenge

Stinky skunks

The chart below shows you how many stinky skunks are hiding on each double page. You can also find out where all the things in the Supreme Spotters' Challenge are hidden.

Pages	Stinky skunks	Supreme Spotters' Challenge
100-101	none	toffee tree
102-103	two	blue pumpkin
104-105	one	spotty rabbit
106-107	four	mouse house
108-109	three	spikey spectacles
110-111	two	lobster
112-113	four	giant lollipop
114-115	one	juggling spider
116-117	two	puzzle parrot
118-119	two	toad on a trike
120-121	three	little yellow dragon!
122-123	two	strange smoke signals
124-125	one	windmill

Did you know?
The friends that Katy and Tim have made in the Puzzle Holiday Park can be found in the other stories in this book too!

PUZZLE SCHOOL

Contents

About this story

This story is about Puzzle School and the children who go there. There are puzzles to solve on every double page. If you get stuck you can look at the answers on pages 159 and 160.

This is Greg. He is a pupil at Puzzle School.

This is Mrs. Smith. She is Greg's teacher at Puzzle School.

On Monday, Mrs. Smith had some news for her class. "It's the school outing tomorrow," she said. "But I'm afraid I won't be here. There will be a new teacher coming for the day. She's called Miss Dibble." Then Mrs. Smith gave everyone a letter for their parents.

Puzzle School

Monday

Dear Parents

Tomorrow each class is going on an outing. I will not be here, but Miss Dibble will be in charge for the day. Come to Puzzle School as usual. Please could all pupils bring a packed lunch.

From
Mrs. Smith
(Class teacher)

Things to spot

Miss Dibble, the new teacher, is a scatterbrain. She's always losing things. She has lost one of these things on every double page, starting on pages 134 and 135.

Brian and Beryl

Brian and Beryl are in Greg's class. They are very naughty. See if you can spot the mischief they get into on every double page, from when Greg arrives at Puzzle School on pages 134-135.

Puzzle School pencils

Can you find the yellow puzzle school pencils? At least one has been left lying around on every double page, starting on page 134.

Getting ready

On Tuesday morning, Greg woke up bright and early, ready for school. He was very excited because today was the day of the school outing. He gobbled down his breakfast and began to get ready for school, but where were all his things? He needed his purple lunch box, his ink pen, his watch, a tennis ball – and his school bag to put everything in.

Can you find the things that Greg needs for school?

Hurry up, Greg, you'll be late.

Where are my school things?

Walking to school

Greg walked to Puzzle School from his house each day. There was always lots to see and do on the way. Today the roads were not very busy but lots of the paths were blocked.

"Don't walk in the road, Greg," his mother called. "And remember, always cross at the striped crossings."

Can you see Puzzle School? (There is a picture of it on page 130.) What route should Greg take to get there?

Bye Ma!

In the playground

Greg arrived safely at Puzzle School. He ran into the playground and looked around for his best friend, Jack. Greg couldn't see him anywhere, but he saw his other friends. Amber was playing hopscotch. Katy was skipping with a red skipping rope. Ben was playing marbles. Ned was kicking a ball. Then at last he saw Jack. He was wearing his yellow baseball cap as usual.

Can you find all of Greg's friends?

I hope Beryl and Brian aren't horrible to me today.

Classroom in a muddle

All the children piled into their classrooms. Greg hung his bag on his peg. He looked at the room. Something was wrong. It was different from yesterday. Then Greg remembered that the painters had been in last night. "Miss Dibble," he said to the new teacher, "everything's been moved. Even our desks are in the wrong places."

"Oh dear," said Miss Dibble, looking puzzled. "I'm afraid I don't know what this room looked like before. Can any of you remember?"

What has changed in the classroom?
Can you find Greg's desk?
(It matches his peg.)

Jobs to do

Soon everything was straightened out and Miss Dibble called out everyone's name.

"Now," she said as she came to the end. "Can somebody tell me what you usually do next?"

"The monitors have their jobs to do," Greg said helpfully, pointing to the chart on the wall. "There are plants to water and the rabbit to feed. There are pencils to sharpen and writing books to hand out. Someone has to wipe the whiteboard, too."

But there was a problem. Things were missing. Where was the rabbit's carrot? What about the whiteboard cleaner? There was no sign of the pencil pot or the yellow writing books, either. And what had happened to the watering can?

Who is doing what job today? Can you find the things they need?

Oh dear.
JOBS
Monday
Beryl
Brian
Tom
Annie
Ben
Tuesday
Jack
Amber
Ned
Katy
Greg
Wednesday
Claire
Joe
Beryl
Brian
Tom
Thursday
Annie
Ben
Jack
Amber
Ned
Friday
Katy
Greg
Claire
Joe
Mrs. Smith
Do your homework
a b c
d e f g
1 2
3

Miss Dibble is confused

Jack, Katy, Amber, Greg and Ned finished their jobs at last.

"Is it nearly time to go on the outing?" asked Greg.

"Soon," said Miss Dibble. "But first we have some work to do."

But Miss Dibble's instructions were all muddled.

"Where should everything really go?" Jack whispered. Greg knew.

Do you?

In the hall

At last everything was tidy. Miss Dibble and her class went to the hall with the rest of the school.

"Where are we going on our outing?" Greg asked Miss Dibble on the way.

"Wait and see," she said as they joined the other classes in the hall. Greg wondered if she'd forgotten.

"Listen carefully," said Mrs. Meady, the head of the school. "One class is going swimming, one class is going ice skating and another class is going to the Dinosaur Park. Mr. Brain's class is visiting the Choco Factory and class four is going to Muddy Farm." She smiled. "The buses are waiting for you outside. But first of all, the children in Mr. Brain's class are going to play their recorders for us."

While Mr. Brain's class was playing their recorders, Greg tried to figure out where his class was going. He saw that some of the children in the other classes had special equipment with them. That made it easier for him to guess.

Where is Greg's class going for their outing?

Bus trouble

Greg and his class were off to the Dinosaur Park! That sounded exciting.

The buses were waiting. Greg and his friends followed Miss Dibble outside the school. Then they climbed on board their bus.

Greg was curious...

SCHOOL
What's wrong?
SOAPY WATER
ENGINE OIL
BRAKE FLUID
Katy jumped down from the bus. "I might be able to help," she said. "My dad's a mechanic." Katy looked at the engine. "I can see the problem," she said.
What has Katy spotted?

Map reading

Stan found some oil in the school garage and filled the engine. At last they were on their way!

"We're off to the Dinosaur Park," everyone sang, as the bus wound its way down the street. Left out of the school gates, then left again, second right, left again and they were at a crossroads.

"Which way now?" called Stan.
"I can't read the map and drive at the same time."

"We'll help!" called Greg and Jack.

Where are they on the map?
Which way should they go?

Stan's Map (not to scale)
= one way only
DINOSAUR PARK
Muddy Farm
Monkey House
Puzzle Ice Rink
Fun-Splash Pool
Savo Supermarket
Hospital
Fire Station
Puzzle School
Choco Factory
Puzzle Garage

Dinosaur park!

At last they arrived at the Dinosaur Park. It was a huge place filled with lots of model dinosaurs.

"You can look around for an hour," Miss Dibble said. "Answer these questions as you go."

She handed everyone pieces of paper. "Leave your packed lunches with me so they don't get squashed, and come back at one o'clock. Have fun!"

Greg and Jack looked at all the dinosaurs in the park, then they tried to answer the questions.

Can you find the answers to the questions?

Lunch time

At one o'clock everybody raced back to Miss Dibble. She handed out the packed lunches. But there were six lunch boxes that looked exactly the same.

"That's mine!" Greg, Jack, Katy, Amber, Ben and Ned, all shouted at once.

"Well what are you each having for lunch?" Miss Dibble asked.

They looked inside the lunch boxes and soon saw whose lunch was whose.

Do you know?

Back to school

After lunch they explored some more. Then it was time to go home.

"Everybody back on the bus," called Miss Dibble.

They lined up and Miss Dibble counted them all.

"Oh dear," she said. "There are two children missing. But who are they – and WHERE are they?"

Greg knew who the missing children were. He thought he remembered seeing them hiding in the park. But where? Then he remembered.

Who is missing? Where were they?

Ah, my little loves!

Time to go home

At last everybody was back on the bus. Stan revved the engine and then they were off, waving goodbye to the Dinosaur Park.

When they got back to Puzzle School, there were lots of people waiting in the playground. Greg, Jack, Amber, Ben, Ned and Katy could see their parents.

Can you?

Toffee time

The next day, Mrs. Smith was back. Miss Dibble came to say goodbye.

"Thank you all for being so helpful," said Miss Dibble. "I had some tasty toffees to give you, but I think I must have dropped them yesterday. Oh dear."

"You had a hole in your pocket," said Greg. "The toffees fell out, so I picked them up. Here they are."

Everyone cheered and munched on their toffees.

Look back through the story. Can you find twelve toffees?

Answers

Pages 132-133
Getting ready
The things that Greg needs are circled here.

Pages 134-135
Walking to school
The way to Puzzle School is marked here.

Pages 136-137
In the playground
Greg's friends are circled here.

Pages 138-139
Classroom in a muddle
The changes are circled here. Greg's desk has a sun on it, like his peg.

Pages 140-141
Jobs to do
It is Tuesday, so Jack is watering the plants, Amber is feeding the rabbit, Ned is sharing the pencils, Katy is handing out the writing books and Greg is wiping the whiteboard. The things that they need are circled here.

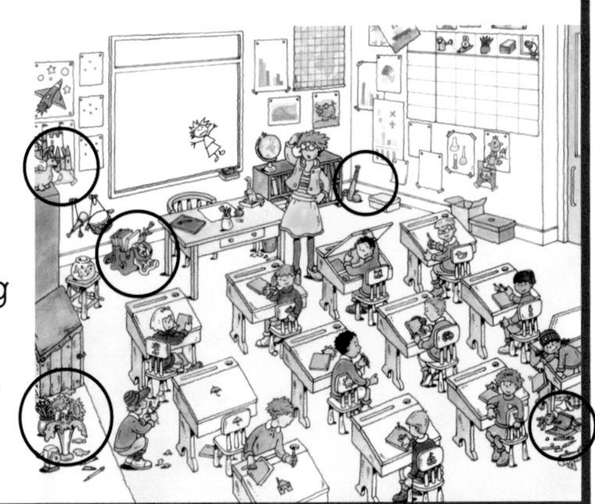

Pages 142-143
Miss Dibble is confused
The rabbit should go in the rabbit hutch. The song sheets should go in the music box. The paints should go in the art cupboard. The pencils should go in the pencil pot. The books should go on the book shelf and Amber's photo should go in her satchel.

Pages 144-145
In the hall
The class circled in red is going skating. The class circled in green is going to Muddy Farm. The class circled in blue is going swimming. Mr. Brain's class is going to the Choco Factory. So Greg's class must be going to the Dinosaur Park.

Pages 146-147
Bus trouble
Katy has spotted that the oil tank is empty!

Pages 148-149
Map reading
Their route from Puzzle School to the Dinosaur Park is marked in red. They are here.

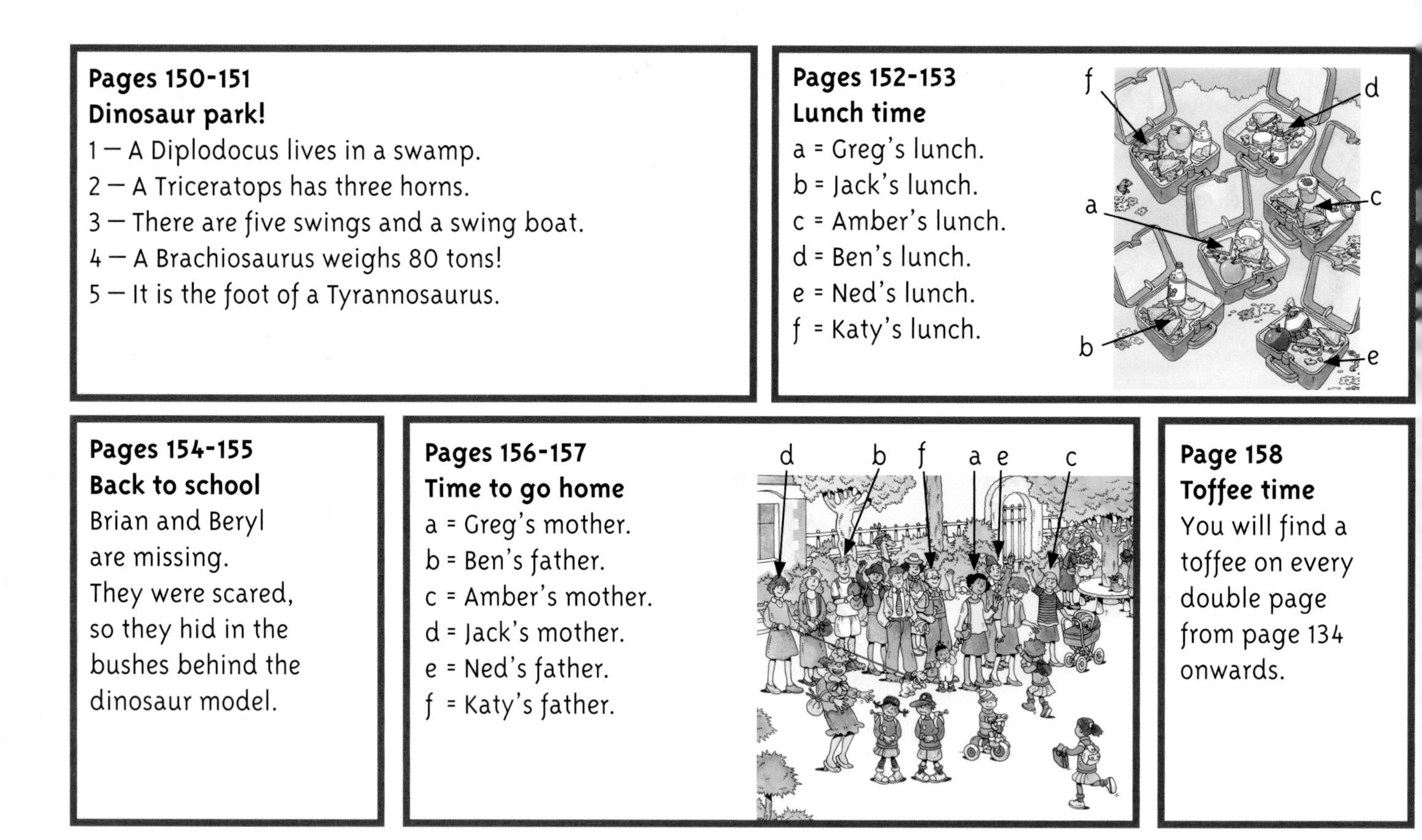

Pages 150-151
Dinosaur park!

1 — A Diplodocus lives in a swamp.
2 — A Triceratops has three horns.
3 — There are five swings and a swing boat.
4 — A Brachiosaurus weighs 80 tons!
5 — It is the foot of a Tyrannosaurus.

Pages 152-153
Lunch time

a = Greg's lunch.
b = Jack's lunch.
c = Amber's lunch.
d = Ben's lunch.
e = Ned's lunch.
f = Katy's lunch.

Pages 154-155
Back to school

Brian and Beryl are missing. They were scared, so they hid in the bushes behind the dinosaur model.

Pages 156-157
Time to go home

a = Greg's mother.
b = Ben's father.
c = Amber's mother.
d = Jack's mother.
e = Ned's father.
f = Katy's father.

Page 158
Toffee time

You will find a toffee on every double page from page 134 onwards.

Did you spot everything?

Puzzle School pencils

Miss Dibble's things

Beryl and Brian

The chart below shows you how many Puzzle School pencils are hiding on each double page. You can also find out where Miss Dibble has lost her things.

Pages	Puzzle School pencils	Miss Dibble's things
134-135	two	scary things book
136-137	three	paint box
138-139	four	pencil
140-141	four	recorder
142-143	three	chalk
144-145	five	cup of tea
146-147	two	glue
148-149	two	key
150-151	four	tissues
152-153	two	scissors
154-155	three	glasses
156-157	none	whistle

Did you remember to watch out for the mischievous Beryl and Brian? Look back through the story again and see if you can spot them.

What happened next?

Since everyone had liked Miss Dibble so much, she was invited back to help with Mrs. Smith's lessons every week. That way, someone could keep an eye on Brian and Beryl too!

PUZZLE PIRATES

Contents

About this story

This story is about a boy named Joe who is learning how to be a pirate at school. Before he can be a real pirate, Joe must earn his pirate cutlass. There is a puzzle to solve on every double page.
If you get stuck, the answers are on pages 191 and 192.

Joe

Pirate School

JOE'S REPORT CARD

Map reading A+
Joe can always find the way

Rope making A+
Excellent at untangling knotty problems

Sword fighting C–
Could try harder

Plank walking C–
Doesn't like getting wet

Joe is a thoughtful, quick-thinking and clever member of the crew, but needs to work on his swashbuckling skills before he can earn his pirate cutlass.

Pirate School has finished for the summer when Joe gets an exciting message from his uncle, Buccaneer Bill. Bill is no ordinary uncle. He is a pirate, and the message sounds serious.

Ahoy there, Joe!

Great news – I've found a treasure map! Trouble is, me old foe, Captain Cutthroat overheard me bragging about the treasure. Off that sneaky seadog sailed with his band of scurvy brigands and I haven't seen him since. They're looking for the treasure too, no doubt. Luckily I still have the map, but I need some help. Come and put your pirate school skills to the test on my new ship, the Salty Seal, and help me find that treasure before Captain Cutthroat.
Meet me at Pirate's Port tomorrow.

Love from your Uncle, Buccaneer Bill x

Joe has heard of Captain Cutthroat. He leads his pirate crew around the high seas, stealing and fighting and generally being bad. Joe can't wait to help Uncle Bill and find the treasure before Cutthroat gets to it.

Things to spot

Joe is excited, but a little worried too. He hasn't been at pirate school long, and his pirate skills need work. But he is very observant. There are lots of things to look out for on the voyage. See if you can help him by spotting one thing on every double page.

maggot

octopus

angry porcupine

hungry crocodile

ghostly pirate

jellyfish

giant rat

stinging wasp

toothy starfish

shark

skull

bald gull

spiky puffer fish

Spot the parrot

Uncle Bill has a parrot named Colin. Colin is a little shy, but you can find him on every double page if you look carefully.

Mermaids' purses

There is a mermaid's purse on every double page. Can you spot them all? Maybe you will find some mermaids along the way to give them to!

Search for the Salty Seal

The next day, Joe skipped down to Pirate's Port to find Uncle Bill's ship, the Salty Seal. Luckily, Uncle Bill had sent him a drawing of the ship, so it should be easy to spot.

But when he arrived at the sea, Joe saw there were lots of boats and ships bobbing around. Which one was the Salty Seal?

Can you spot the Salty Seal?

SIZE 12
SAILS 4 SALE
BARREL OF LIMES

All aboard!

Joe found a little boat and rowed across to the Salty Seal. Uncle Bill beamed down at him.

"Ahoy there, Joe! You made it. Now, climb aboard!"

Joe gazed at the maze of ropes and ladders that covered the side of the ship. How would he ever climb up?

Uncle Bill seemed to read his mind. "You can do it, lad," he called. "Climb from rope to rope and up the ladders and you'll be here in no time. Watch out for the slippery green seaweed, though. And the giant purple-clawed lobsters will give you a nasty nip."

Can you help Joe find a safe way up onto the deck?

Meet the crew

Joe pulled himself up the last ladder and clambered over the rail, landing in an exhausted heap at Uncle Bill's feet. Uncle Bill picked him up in his beefy arms and gave him a swashbuckling sque-e-e-e-e-ze.

"Oo arr, Joe, am I glad to see you," he boomed. "Now, meet me crew!" Bill gestured to a motley band of pirates. "They're all new recruits like you, and I'm still learning their names. Let's see, who is who?"

Look carefully at the pirates' names. Can you help Joe decide who is who?

There's Peg-leg Poll and Mophead Mick, One-eyed Jem and Rufus Redhead. Oh, and don't forget Stripes, the ship's cat.

Treasure map

Joe guessed everyone's names correctly. Then the ladders, ropes and nets on the side of the ship were pulled up and the Salty Seal was ready to set sail. Bill sat Joe down at the captain's table and spread out a big map before him.

"We've got to set a course for Deadly Isle," Bill explained. "That's where the treasure is buried. The instructions are written on the map, but me old pirate brain ain't as quick as she used to be. Can ye help me find Deadly Isle, Joe?"

Can you follow the clues to find Deadly Isle?

Clues:

N
W E
S

Start at port and sail North East –
To the red ragged rocks, then East to the beast.
On to pink seaweed cove, then North to Green Land,
West from there and you're close at hand.
With the yellow-tailed dolphins, play awhile
Then North West past a monster to Deadly Isle!

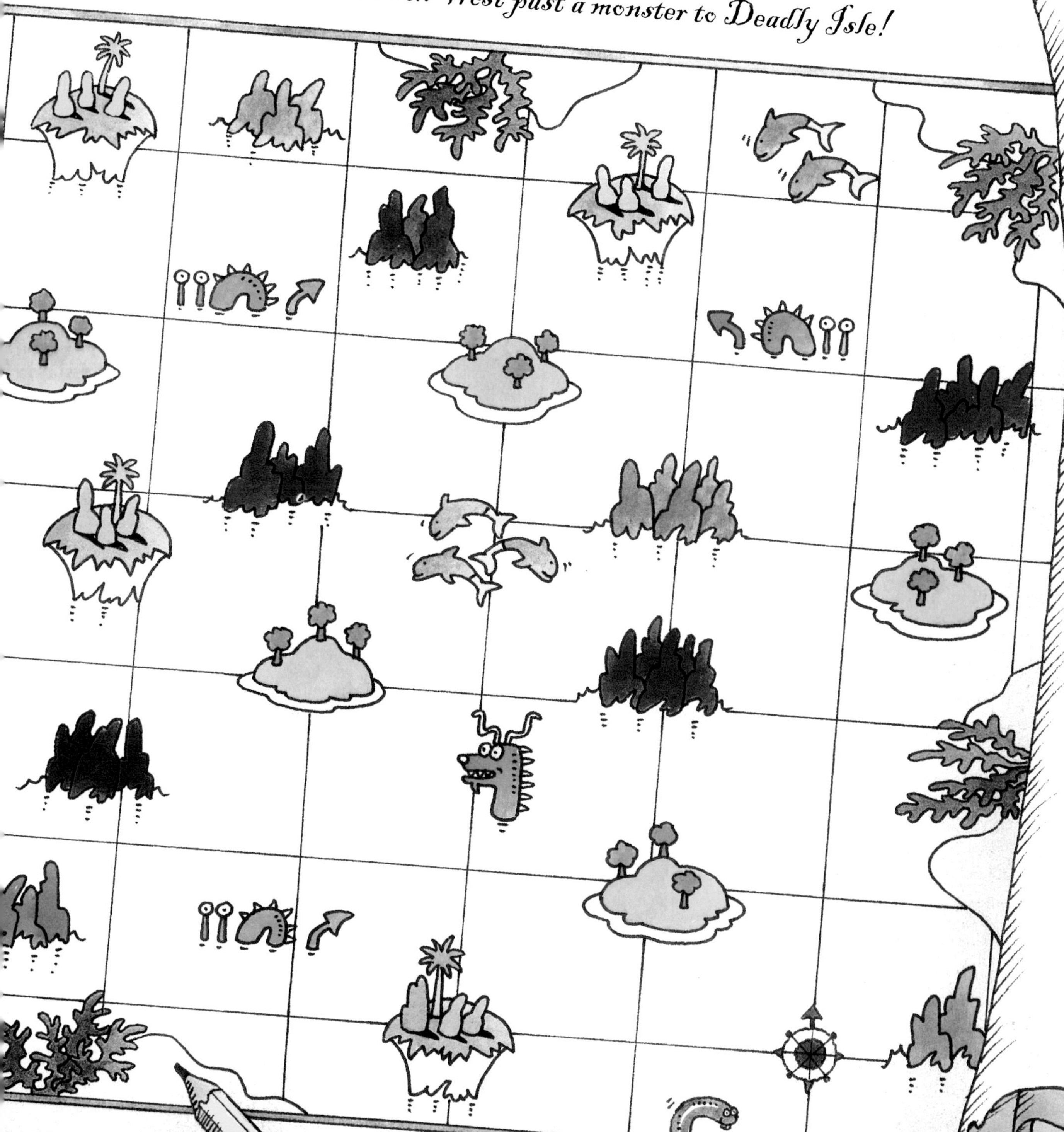

Sea voyage

Joe helped Bill to plot a course for Deadly Isle. Several yo ho hos later, the Salty Seal set sail on the search for treasure. Uncle Bill was at the wheel. Joe, who was good at map reading, was navigating.

Together they journeyed...

"Land ahoy! Deadly Isle – dead ahead!"

"Ye did it lad, ye led us here!" cried Bill. Joe felt as pleased as pirate punch. But as he took a closer look at Deadly Isle, he spotted something he had seen earlier that day. Something that made his heart sink to the bottom of his boots.

What has Joe spotted, and who does it belong to?

Rocky reefs

Uncle Bill's face went as purple as a parrot's plume. "How in barnacles did Cutthroat get here first?"

Joe took a closer look at the ship. "I can't see anyone on board," he said. "Cutthroat must be ashore."

"Let's get there and find the treasure, then," Bill cried.

Joe smiled. "I've got a better plan. Launch our row boat, Uncle Bill. We're going aboard that ship."

"I may only have one eye," said Jem,
"but even I can see the rocky reefs in the way."

"Let's get through them quickly," said Joe.
"I have this strange feeling we're being watched..."

Can you find a safe way through the rocky reefs to Cutthroat's ship? Some of the rocks have eyes – can you see how many?

Joe's plan

Safely through the rocky reefs, Joe tried to tell everyone his plan. But the wind was whistling and his words were blown away.

Can you put the pictures in the right order and discover Joe's plan?

and when the ship is at sea, we will pick you up.
We might meet Cutthroat and his crew there, but with their ship out to sea, they'll be stranded!
Then we'll all row back to Deadly Isle to look for the treasure,
where Bill, Rufus, Jem and Peg will climb aboard and set sail.

Deadly Isle

Joe's plan worked! They were ashore Deadly Isle, with Cutthroat's ship far out to sea. Just then, there was a rustle in the bushes.

"Cutthroat!" Bill hissed.

"No, worse!" yelled Joe as a band of bone-shaking pirate skeletons lurched towards them, teeth grinning and swords slashing.

"Now I know why they call this Deadly Isle!" Bill gasped as he lunged forward.

With a mighty swipe,
CLUNK
a head was off –
and another, until finally...
"We did it!" cried Bill. "Every last one of 'em down, me hearties!"
Joe shivered as he scanned the scattered skeletons. Pieces of paper fluttered among the jumble of bones. All the pieces of paper had writing on them and two of them looked very useful indeed.
"I think the skeletons were hiding the secret of the treasure," Joe said slowly. "There are two useful clues here!"
I wish I'd had a pirate cutlass for that battle.
BOO HOO!
Treasure in Creepy Cavern
SHAKE RATTLE ROLL
Creepy Cavern next to tall palm tree
DEM BONES DEM BONES
PARTY TONIGHT
FOR SALE
ONE FUNNY BONE - HARDLY USED
We are the ISLE'S GUARDS Bones
Can you spot the useful clues?

Creepy Cavern

Bill read the clues and gave a low whistle. "So the treasure is in the Creepy Cavern?"

"And there's the tall palm tree next to it," Joe cried.

Sure enough, towering above the small shrubs and bushes was a palm tree, taller than all the rest. They set off...

until – Creepy Cavern! Bill was about to try the door, when suddenly, a man with a long beard jumped out at them...

"Yes sir," Joe stuttered in surprise.

Roger chuckled. "Then you'll need to unlock the door. You seem a polite young man so I'll help you. Somewhere nearby lie seven hidden objects like the ones on this scroll. Find them, place them in the holes in the door, and it will magically unlock."

Can you find all the objects they need?

Monster maze

C-r-e-e-e-a-k. The door swung open and into Creepy Cavern they crept.

"Oh, I almost forgot!" Roger called. "A cyclops guards the trapdoor to the treasure. You'll need to find him some orange sea biscuits to munch so he'll let you through."

Joe shivered. A cyclops was bad enough, but he had thought of something else.

"If I remember my pirate geography lessons," he whispered to Bill, "Creepy Caverns are always home to Mighty Spiders and Vampire Bats. We must be careful which passage we take."

Can you find the way along the twisty passages to the trapdoor? Don't forget to look for the orange sea biscuits on the way!

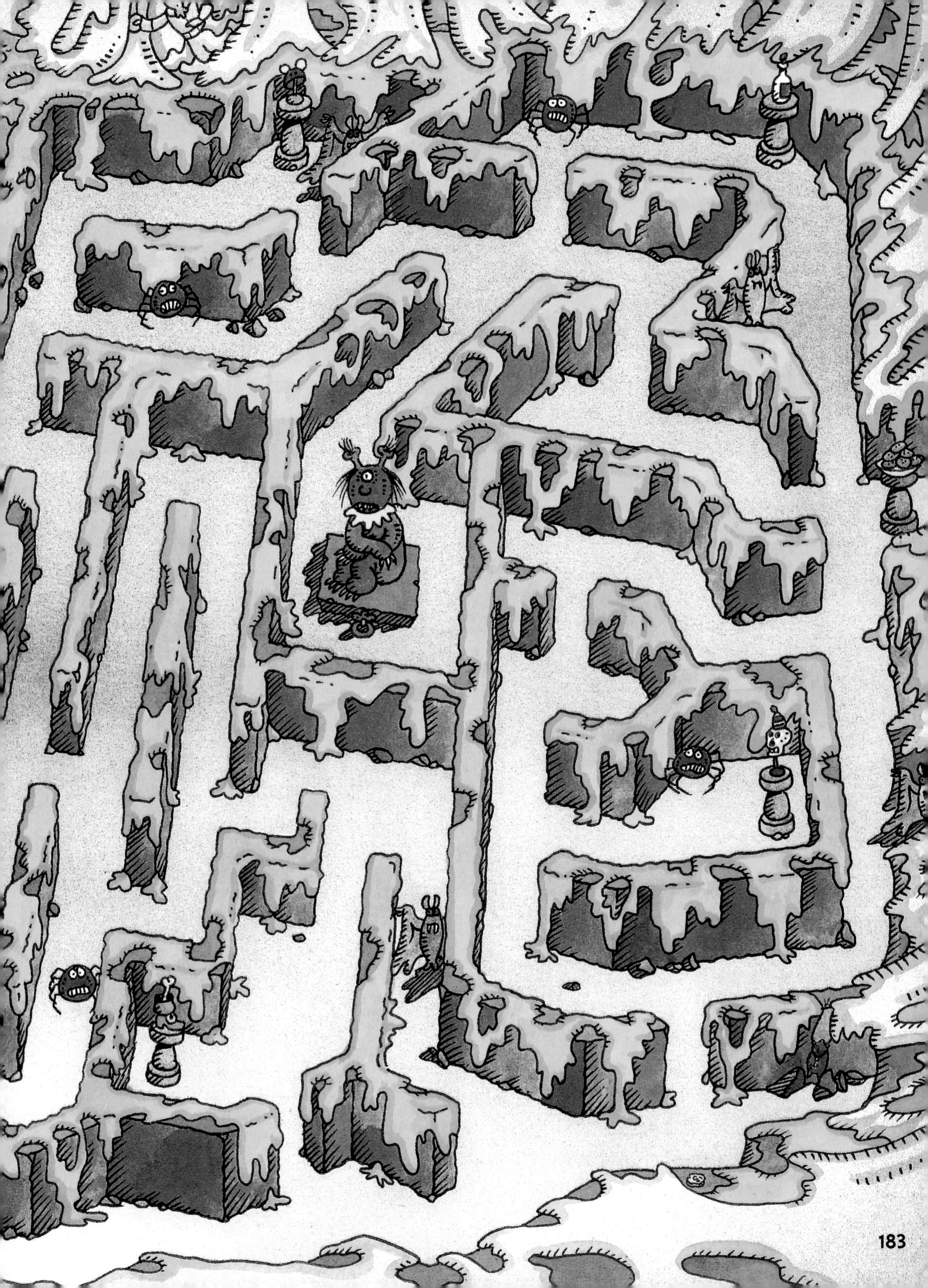

Mermaid misery

The trapdoor opened to reveal a slide that led them down to an underground cave.

"What the...?" Bill began.

Hanging from the roof was the treasure chest! Dangling next to it was a key. But there were also mermaids, trapped in netted ponds, above which hung terrible sea monsters.

"Please help," cried a merboy. "One of these ropes leads to the key that will unlock us. But pull the wrong rope and those deadly sea monsters will spill out onto my five sisters. Can you set us free?"

Bill was puzzled. "Where do the ropes begin and end?"

"Look," said Joe. "The ropes tied to the rocks on the ground are all different shades. By matching them to the ropes hanging from the roof, I can see which rope leads where."

Can you find the right rope to release the key – and the rope to release the treasure chest too?

The key to
unlock us all opens
the treasure
chest too!
That creepy
cyclops put us
here!

The treasure!

The key was freed and the chest was safely lowered down. Joe unlocked the mermaids and with a flash and a sparkle they swam out of the cave through an underground river. Joe and the crew followed them along the bank, carrying the chest with them. But to their dismay, they had walked straight into a trap.

"Ambush!" cried Captain Cutthroat. "All we had to do was follow ye scurvy dogs to the treasure and let ye do the hard work. Ha, it was almost too easy!"

But then Cutthroat yawned, as beautiful music filled the air. The mermaids were singing a magic tune and everyone began to feel very sleepy. Joe stole a quick glance at the little merboy.

"Quick," Joe whispered to Bill and the crew as Cutthroat's men began to nod off. "Find the shell headphones and cover your ears. Then you won't fall asleep."

Can you find the six shell headphones?

Pirate party

Quietly, Joe and the gang rowed back to the Salty Seal and opened the chest with the mermaids' key. Inside was the most amazing pirate treasure. In the middle of the jewels and glittery stuff there was a special message. It read,

"There's a gold cutlass here, treasure rare;
it can be claimed by one who dares.
If this pirate is clever, it will be his – forever."

"Well, if you can find it here, the gold cutlass is yours, Joe," said Bill. "Your quick thinking saved the day more than any swashbuckling skills. You have proved yourself a worthy pirate indeed."

Can you spot Joe's gold cutlass? Can you see what has happened to Cutthroat and his crew?

Pirate school

Back at school after his summer pirate adventure, Joe was proud to show off his new cutlass to all his friends.

"And I found these golden coins on my journey," he grinned. "There's one for each of you."

"Let's hear three cheers for pirate Joe," cried his teacher, and Joe's friends' voices raised the roof.

Go back through the story and spot the golden coin Joe collected for each pupil. There's one on every double page.

Answers

pages 164-165

pages 166-167

pages 168-169

pages 170-171

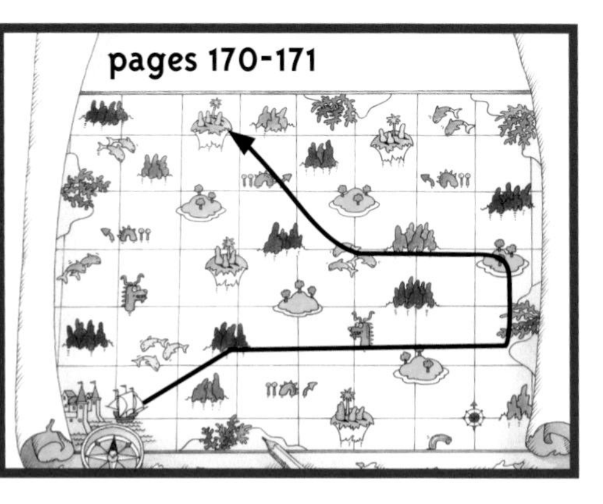

pages 172-173

pages 174-175

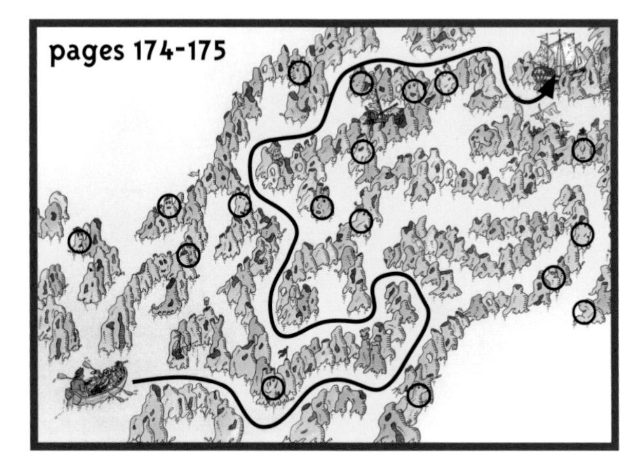

pages 176-177

1. First, we'll all row to the Ghastly Galleon,
2. where Bill, Rufus, Jem and Peg will climb aboard and set sail.
3. Meanwhile, Mophead and I will row behind the Galleon,
4. and when the ship is at sea, we will pick you up.
5. Then we'll all row back to Deadly Isle to look for the treasure.
6. We might meet Cutthroat and his crew there, but with their ship out to sea, they'll be stranded!

pages 178-179

The clues say:

pages 180-181

pages 184-185 The red rope releases the treasure chest. The pink rope releases the key.

pages 188-189 Cutthroat and his crew are stranded on Deadly Isle with the cyclops!

page 190 Did you spot the golden coin on each double page? (There isn't one on pages 162 and 163.)

Did you spot everything?

Did you spot Colin the parrot on every double page?

And did you find the mermaids' purses?

The list below shows you where the things to spot are hidden.

pages	objects	pages	objects
164-165	giant rat	178-179	skull
166-167	shark	180-181	stinging wasp
168-169	octopus	182-183	ghostly pirate
170-171	maggot	184-185	spiky puffer fish
172-173	hungry crocodile	186-187	angry porcupine
174-175	jellyfish	188-189	toothy starfish
176-177	bald gull		

What happened next?

Back at school, Joe worked hard on his sword-fighting skills. With the help of his trusty gold cutlass, it wasn't long before he became the class champion!

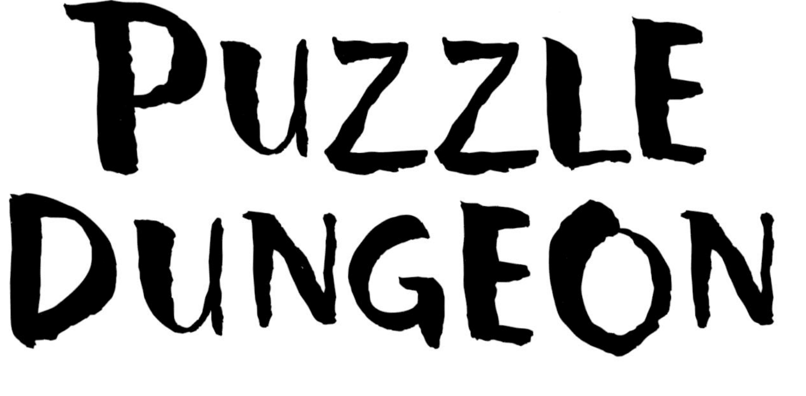

Contents

About this story

This story is about Carla, her cat Ginger and their adventures in Puzzle Dungeon. There is a puzzle on every double page. See if you can solve them all. If you get stuck, you can look at the answers on pages 223 and 224.

Puzzle Dungeon is dark and mysterious and lies deep underground. It's not far away, but Carla doesn't know anyone who has ever been there before. Until now that is...

...Carla has just had a letter from her best friend, Billy. Billy wants to be an inventor when he grows up. He has gone down to Puzzle Dungeon to try out his latest experiment. Read his letter to find out more.

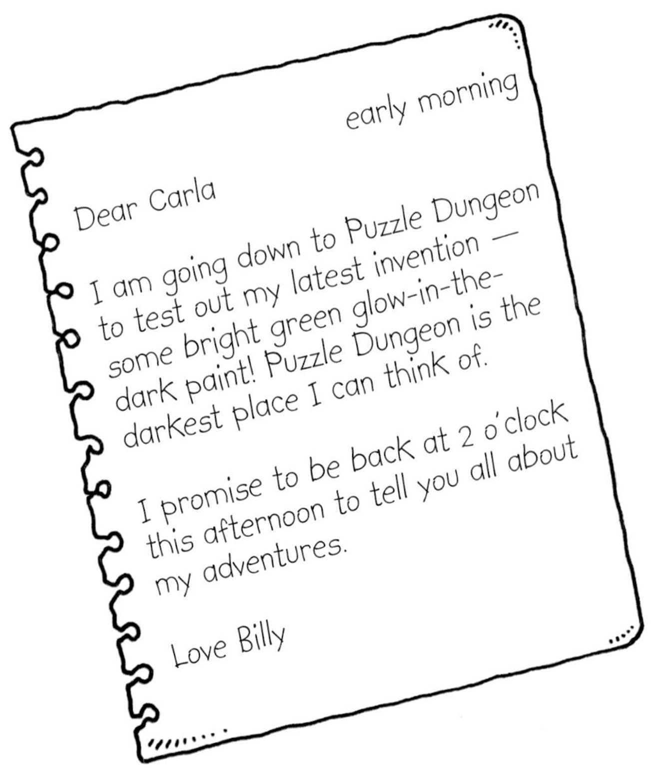

early morning

Dear Carla

I am going down to Puzzle Dungeon to test out my latest invention — some bright green glow-in-the-dark paint! Puzzle Dungeon is the darkest place I can think of.

I promise to be back at 2 o'clock this afternoon to tell you all about my adventures.

Love Billy

Carla was worried by the letter. She had heard some very spooky stories about Puzzle Dungeon. Spiders as big as houses, scary monsters and deadly snakes were said to live there. Billy was very brave to go down on his own. Carla hoped he would be all right.

Things to spot

Billy might be brave, but he is also very good at losing things. You will find something he has dropped on almost every double page, starting on pages 198-199. You can see a picture of all the things to look out for here.

comic book

bandage

paintbrush

jumping frog

inventor's goggles

toffee

teddy

chewing gum

can of paint

little purse

test tube

Skeleton Sid

Sid the skeleton lives in Puzzle Dungeon. Look out for him on almost every double page. Don't worry, he is quite friendly – but a little shy.

Dungeon beetles

Watch out for the flying beetles who live in Puzzle Dungeon. You will find them on almost every double page.

You'll only find us in the dungeon!

Billy is late

It was 3 o'clock. Billy had said he would be back at two, but there was still no sign of him. Carla was worried. Billy was good at losing things. What if he had lost himself in Puzzle Dungeon? There was only one thing to do. She would have to go and find him.

Carla thought hard. If she was going to a dungeon, she would need some dungeon equipment. She decided to take her bright green backpack, a bar of chocolate, her hat with the lamp on top, her jester's stick, a penguin mirror and a yellow handkerchief. But where were they all?

Can you find them?

Cousin Sophie

Poppy
My Friend

Billy and his
parents

CHOC

ATLAS

BRAVE
DUNGEON
EXPLORER
Ma and Pa
GINGER
POP
SNAKES AND LADDERS

Which way?

Carla gathered up her equipment and set off. Puzzle Dungeon lay deep underground beneath a ruined castle, a short way from her village.

Carla knew that the only way into Puzzle Dungeon was through a little doorway in the hillside, but when she arrived, she saw lots of little doorways. Which one led to Puzzle Dungeon?

Then Carla remembered something. An old tale said that the door to Puzzle Dungeon was directly underneath an apple tree, and that five blue and five yellow flowers always bloomed around it. Carla looked closely at the doors and saw that the old tale was true. Now she knew which one to go through.

Which door leads to Puzzle Dungeon?

Underground!

Carla slowly pushed open the rusty door. She shone her light into the darkness and gulped nervously. She felt rather scared, but Billy was her best friend and she had to find him. She couldn't turn back now.

With Ginger following close behind, Carla began the journey deep down into the mysterious underground world of Puzzle Dungeon...

They climbed down a ladder and reached the bottom of the hole. In the gloom, Carla saw a large cave, with five doors leading from it. She groaned. More doors!

As she looked around she saw something that made her think Billy had been here before. Now she knew which way he had gone.

Which way should she go to follow Billy?

Creepy cavern

Carla followed the fluorescent footprints through the door. Then they disappeared. Billy's paint wasn't working very well!

Carla stopped short. She was in a deep cavern filled with thick green slime. On the other side was an archway. It was the start of another path, and it seemed to be the only way to go next. But to get to it, she would have to cross the cavern.

Then Carla saw a notice. She read it carefully and looked back at the cavern. She saw the giant pillars rising from the slime. The way looked easy enough. Carla wondered if Billy had already gone across. She hoped he hadn't fallen in. Carla would do what the notice said, being very careful where she stepped.

Can you find the safe way across the pillars?

Dungeon prisoners

Carla jumped off the last pillar and ran through the archway into a crumbling stone chamber. Iron rings hung from the walls, and ropes lay on the ground.

"This must have been where the dungeon prisoners were kept," Carla shuddered.

There was no way out apart from back the way they'd come. Or was there? As Carla read the carvings on the walls, she saw that one of them held a back to front clue. There was another way out of the chamber after all!

How can they get out of the chamber?

NASTY PUNISHMENT
DUNGEONS ARE DREADFUL
The Prisoners
It's quite a friendly dungeon really.
Find a ring that looks like this. Pull it and a secret door will open.
HERE I SIT IN THE GLOOM LOCKED INSIDE THIS DUNGEON ROOM.
MONSTER
WEEK'S MENU
MON - BREAD + WATER
TUES - BREAD + WATER
WEDS - PIE + CHIPS
THURS - BREAD + WATER
FRI, SAT, SUN - WATER + BREAD
DUNGEON RULES
NO PARTYING
NO SINGING
NO VISITORS
NO ESCAPING!
DOG MONSTER
UNDERWORLD
GOING UNDERGROUND
The Rack
T.V. GUIDE
POP

Scary monsters

Carla pulled the ring and the secret door swung open. She stepped through it and almost jumped out of her skin. Giants and ogres, mummies and monsters stared back at her! But when she looked closer, she saw they were only statues.

Carla breathed a sigh of relief, when suddenly she noticed something else that made her jump. Was it her imagination, or was she being watched? Not by the unblinking eyes of the statues, but by some smaller creatures peering out from them.

How many of these creatures can you see?

Picture map

Four little creatures jumped out from their hiding places and said they were dungeon dwellers. They were quite friendly. What's more, they had seen Billy.

They showed Carla a map and tried to tell her where Billy had gone next. But they all had different ideas. Carla was confused. They couldn't all be right. She looked at the map and realized only one suggestion fitted the pictures exactly. This was where Billy had gone.

Can you see which suggestion fits the picture map?

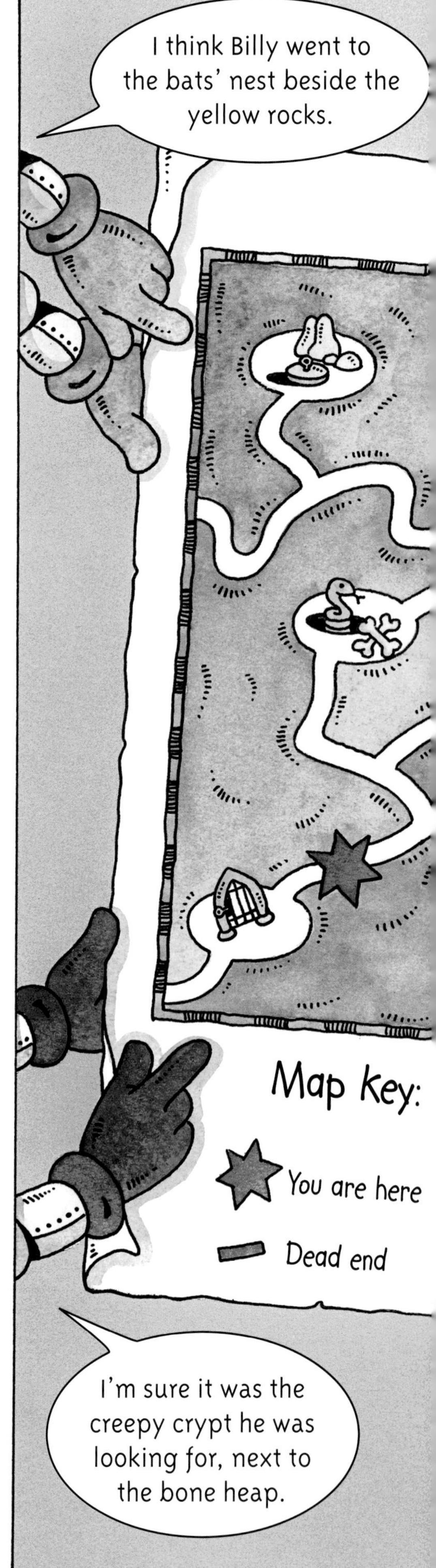

Perhaps he went to look at the yellow crystal at the waterfall.
Snake pit
Yellow crystal
Red rocks
Prison cell
Waterfall
Well
Red crystal
Earth mound
Creepy crypt
Bone heap
Bats' nest
Yellow rocks
He may have gone to the well, next to the red rocks.

Hungry snakes

Carla set off for the well with her new friends. But just before they turned a corner, the dungeon dwellers stopped.

"We don't dare go any further, Carla," they said. "There are poisonous snakes near here. You are taller and braver than us. If you can find a plain green mushroom for each snake to eat, you can pass them safely."

Can you find the green mushrooms? You will need one for each snake.

FAKE SNAKE
LAUNDRY BASKET

Mouse trouble

Carla and Ginger the cat left the chomping snakes and hurried on their way. Soon they came to the room where the well was supposed to be, but there was no sign of it. All Carla could see were mice, playing in the room. They looked as if they were having fun. Carla stood in the doorway wondering what to do next, when she was startled by a loud MEOW from Ginger.

Ginger pounced into the room, and in a flash he had chased the mice away. Carla shook her head. She felt sorry for the mice. She wanted to tell them not to be scared. She knew Ginger wouldn't really hurt them. But now she couldn't see them anywhere.

Can you see where all the mice have gone? (Have you spotted the cover of the well?)

Spider's web

The mice weren't taking any chances with Ginger in the room, so they stayed well hidden.

Carla walked over to the well. Using her jester's stick, she levered off the cover. It slid away easily. Perhaps Billy had already been here... Carla peered into the inky blackness below. She couldn't give up her search now. The only way was down.

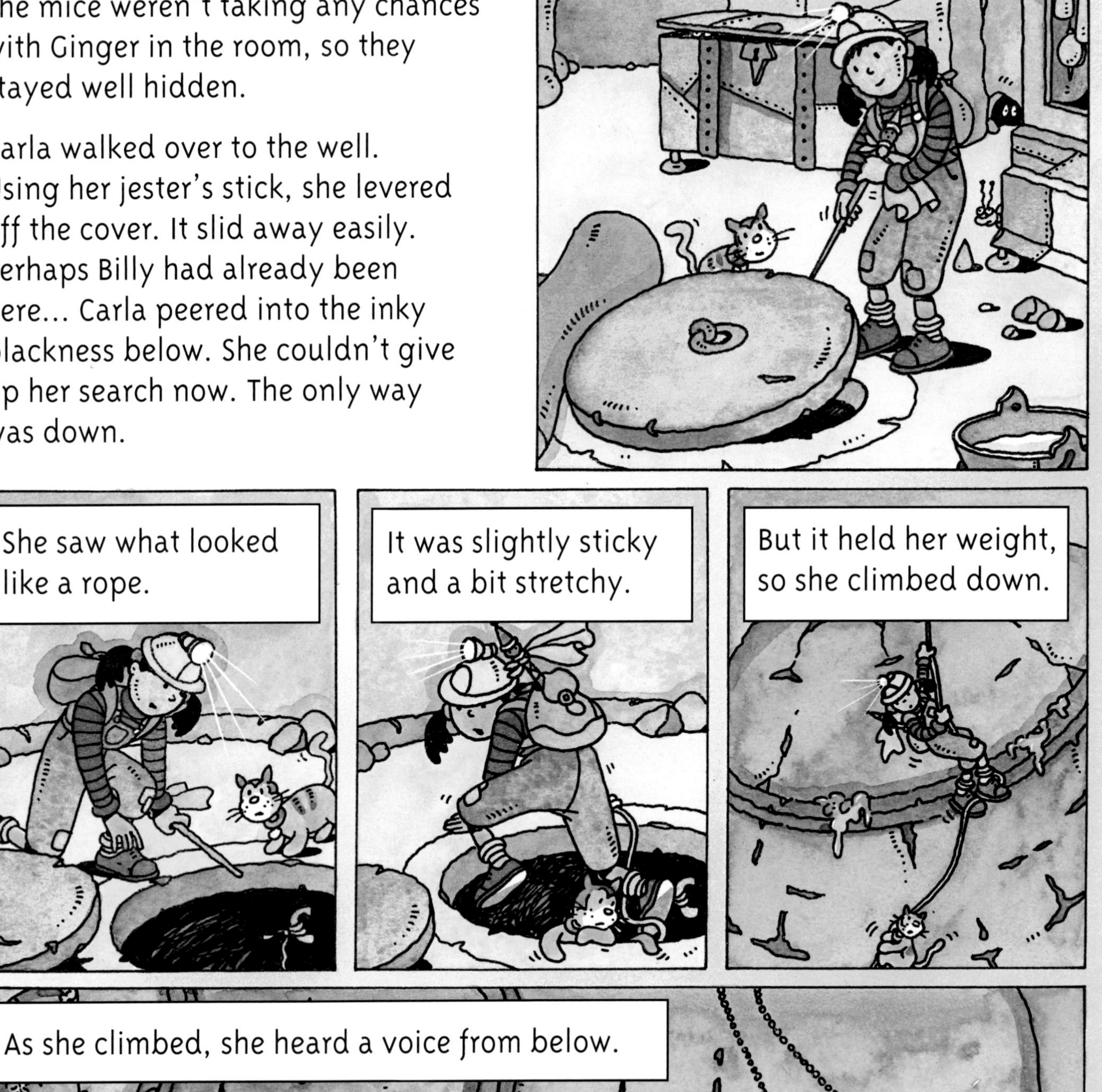

She was at the top of a giant spider's web! It was surprisingly strong, rather like an enormous climbing frame. Carla saw that if she was very careful, she could crawl along and down the web without waking the baby spiders.

Can you find a safe way down the web?

Shiny cavern

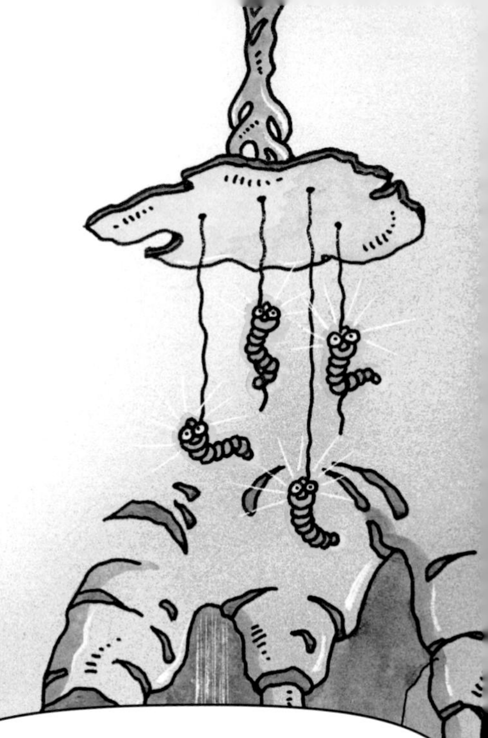

Carla and Ginger scrambled safely down the web and through a stone archway. They were in a shimmery blue cave. Twinkling green lights sparkled all around. Carla looked closely and saw that the lights were glow worms. What's more, they seemed to be singing a strangely soothing song.

Then Carla saw Billy. He was sound asleep. She tried to call out to him, but she was feeling rather drowsy. From far away she heard a voice. It was Sid the skeleton! She had to do what he said, and fast.

Can you do what Sid says?

My turn to help has come at last.
You'll sleep as well, if you're not fast.
So find the magic flask-and-cup,
Give Billy a drink and he'll wake up.

Secret lake

Carla took a sip from the magic cup. At once she felt wide awake. She poured some magic liquid into Billy's mouth. He woke up and rubbed his eyes. He was very surprised to see Carla.

"Did you see the glow worms, Carla?" he said. "They shine in the dark much better than my paint does."

"Let's go home," said Carla. "It's getting late."

Suddenly, Ginger darted off through a small hole in between some rocks.

"Come back Ginger!" Carla called.

But Ginger had disappeared.

"We'll have to go and find him," said Carla. "We can't leave him here. Who knows what could happen to him?"

They followed Ginger through the hole and found themselves on the shore of an underground lake. Light from a raised portcullis streamed across the water. Maybe there was another way out of the dungeon! They could use a boat to get across the water, but they didn't all look very safe.

Which boat do you think they should use?

Home at last!

They jumped into the little boat, pedalled through the open portcullis and out of Puzzle Dungeon. They blinked their eyes in the bright sunshine and saw they were in the middle of a lake. People were standing on the shore.

"Where are we?" asked Billy, still groggy from sleep.

Carla knew exactly where they were, and what's more, she could see some very familiar faces.

Do you know where they are, and do you recognize some of the people here?

That evening

Later that evening, Billy and Carla sat sipping cocoa at Carla's house. As they sat, they talked about their adventures in Puzzle Dungeon.

"I think I'll be testing my inventions above ground from now on," said Billy. "Puzzle Dungeon is a bit scary for me."

Ginger purred sleepily and dreamed about the dungeon dwellers. What funny creatures they were, and what strange metal objects they had made.

Look back through the story again. What do you think the dungeon dwellers might have made?

Answers

Pages 196-197 Billy is late
The six pieces of dungeon equipment are circled here.

Pages 198-199 Which way?
This door leads to Puzzle Dungeon.

Pages 200-201 Underground!
Carla should follow Billy through this door. She has seen some of his green glow-in-the-dark paint.

Pages 202-203 Creepy cavern
The safe way across the pillars is marked in red.

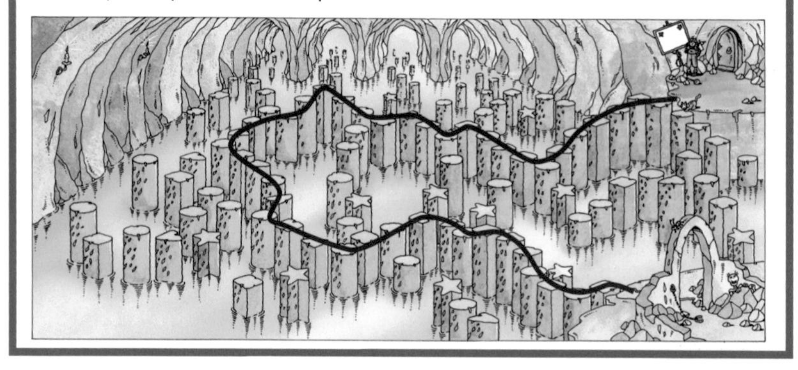

Pages 204-205 Dungeon prisoners
They can get out of the chamber by reading this message in mirror writing and doing what it says.

Here is the ring they must pull.

Here is what the message says the right way around:
Find a ring that looks like this. Pull it and a secret door will open.

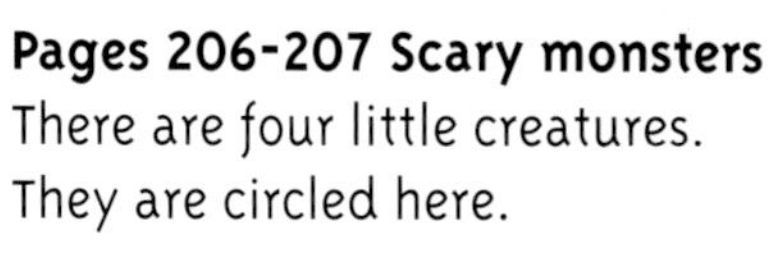

Pages 206-207 Scary monsters
There are four little creatures. They are circled here.

Pages 208-209 Picture map
Billy has gone to the well next to the red rocks. This is the only place that is really on the map. All the other suggestions don't match up.

Pages 210-211 Hungry snakes
The green mushrooms are circled here. There are ten, one for each snake.

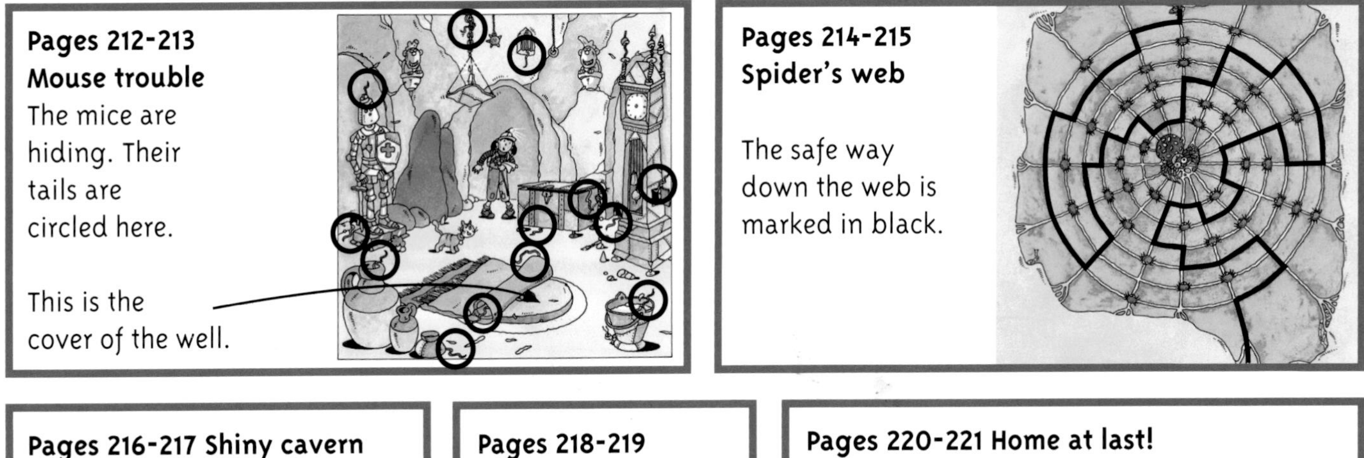

Pages 212-213
Mouse trouble
The mice are hiding. Their tails are circled here.

This is the cover of the well.

Pages 214-215
Spider's web

The safe way down the web is marked in black.

Pages 216-217 Shiny cavern
Sid tells Carla to look for the magic flask-and-cup.
They are here.

Pages 218-219
Secret lake
They should use this boat. It is the safest.

Pages 220-221 Home at last!
They are at the lake in their village.
You have seen a picture of it on page 198.
Carla can see her parents, and Billy's parents. You can see pictures of them on pages 196-197.

Carla's parents are circled in red.
Billy's parents are circled in black.

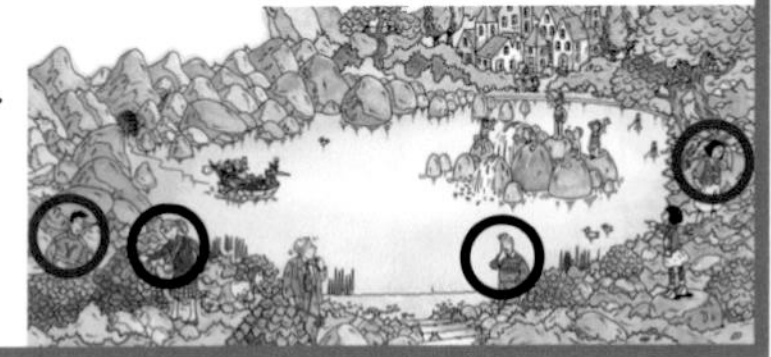

Did you spot everything?

Dungeon beetles

Did you remember to count the dungeon beetles and find one of Billy's things on almost every double dungeon page? The chart below tells you where to find everything.

Billy's things

Pages	Beetles	Billy's things
198-199	none	little purse
200-201	two	bandage
202-203	two	test tube
204-205	three	comic book
206-207	four	toffee
208-209	three	inventor's goggles
210-211	three	chewing gum
212-213	three	paintbrush
214-215	three	can of paint
216-217	two	teddy bear
218-219	three	jumping frog
220-221	none	none

Sid the skeleton

Did you spot Sid the skeleton down in Puzzle Dungeon? He enjoyed watching Carla's dungeon journey, and he was happy to help at the end!

What happened next?
It wasn't long before Jasper and the lobsters realized that the treasure was fake, and they were soon up to their usual tricks. But they knew better than to try to steal the King's crown again!

PUZZLE OCEAN

Contents

About this story

This story is about a girl named Rosie and her amazing adventure in the underwater world of Puzzle Ocean. There are puzzles to solve on every double page. If you get stuck, you can look at the answers on pages 255 and 256.

Rosie's adventure begins one Sunday afternoon at the seaside. Whenever Rosie visits the seaside she plays with her friend Milly. There is something very special about Milly which you will find out later on.

All sorts of fantastic things lie at the bottom of Puzzle Ocean. There's even a pirate ship called the Jolly Dodger. Once there was treasure on board the Jolly Dodger. Now the treasure is scattered across the ocean floor.

Things to spot

Rosie's friend Milly collects the Jolly Dodger pirate treasure as they go. There is a piece of treasure on every double page. Can you collect it too? It might be useful later on. Here are the things to look out for.

diamond dolphin

emerald eye patch

rum

gold locket

piece of eight

gem-encrusted telescope

silver cutlass

ruby ring

glass goblet

pearl necklace

precious perfume

magic treasure-collecting bag

Yellow-clawed lobsters

Beware of the yellow-clawed lobsters! They like pinching things. Can you spot a yellow-clawed lobster on every double page? The lobsters have a sneaky friend called Jasper. You will meet him later on.

Blue oysters

Puzzle Ocean is home to the rare blue ocean oysters. There is at least one blue oyster hiding shyly on each double page. See if you can find them all.

On the beach

On Sunday afternoon, Rosie was paddling in the ocean. Suddenly she saw a bottle bobbing in the water. Rosie picked it up. Inside was a message. What's more, it was for her!

But Rosie wasn't surprised. It was from her friend Milly. Milly always sent Rosie a message in a bottle when she wanted to play. But as Rosie read the note, she gasped. It said there was trouble in Puzzle Ocean! She had to find Milly.

Where is Milly?
Can you see what is special about her?

Ocean trouble

Rosie rushed over to the blue rock pool. Sure enough, her friend Milly the mermaid was waiting.

"Something dreadful has happened in Puzzle Ocean, Rosie," Milly said. "We need some human help."

Milly began to explain...

"Look Rosie. There's Jasper now,"
Milly cried. "And he's got the crown."
Can you see Jasper?

Milly's plan

Jasper dived beneath the waves with the golden crown and disappeared.

"Quick Rosie, we must follow Jasper and get the crown back," said Milly. "Come with me and I'll explain how you can help."

She took Rosie to a cave away from the busy beach and began to tell her what she had to do...

"Jasper must be taking the crown to his Puzzle Ocean home," Milly said. "It has a secret entrance, but we'll never find that in time. The only other way in is over a sand bank. I can't walk across the sand bank with my fishy tail, but you could, Rosie. Will you help?"

"Of course I will, Milly," Rosie said bravely.

"Thank you," Milly cried. "First we will have to journey deep into Puzzle Ocean to find Jasper's home. I'll make something magic to help you breathe underwater. I need some red seaweed, a blue pebble, a yellow pebble, a green starfish and two green flippers. Can you help me, Rosie?"

Can you find everything?

Underwater

Rosie found everything. Milly said some magic mermaid words. In a flash, Rosie was holding a shimmery cobweb.

"Slip this under your top, Rosie," Milly said. "It will help you breathe like a fish. The flippers are for your feet."

Milly took Rosie's hand as they dived beneath the waves.

This was the first time Rosie had been under the water. She could breathe but swimming wasn't so easy. Suddenly she bumped into an octopus. It squirted a cloud of green ink and scared all the sea creatures. When the ink cleared, several things had changed – and Milly had vanished.

Can you spot the differences? Where is Milly?

A fishy problem

Rosie helped Milly out from behind the chest where she was looking at a scrap of paper. The chest was empty, except for one piece of treasure which they picked up. They put it in their bag and paddled on. Before long they found themselves at St. Fisher's school.

"Naughty Jasper passed by earlier and caused a terrible commotion," wailed Mrs. Mullet, the teacher. "Now these little fishes are being naughty too. Some are in the wrong classes and some are hiding. Can you help me sort them out? There should be six rainbow fish in the art class, five orange clowny fish in the juggling class, four blue stickybacks in the music class and seven green goober fish in the sports class."

Can you find all the fish and send them to the right classes?

St. Fisher's School

MUSIC CLASS
four stickybacks
JUGGLING CLASS
five clowny fish
SPORTS CLASS
seven goober fish
ART CLASS
six rainbow fish

Overboard!

Soon all the naughty fish were in the right classes. Mrs. Mullet was very pleased.

Rosie and Milly swam on. Up above, shapes moved on the water.

"Fishing boats!" Rosie said.

"Look," said Milly. "They have caught some very strange objects. I wonder if Jasper is responsible for this tangle of trouble."

"Listen, Milly," Rosie said. "Everyone thinks they have caught very big fish!"

Can you untangle all the ropes and see what each boat has really caught?

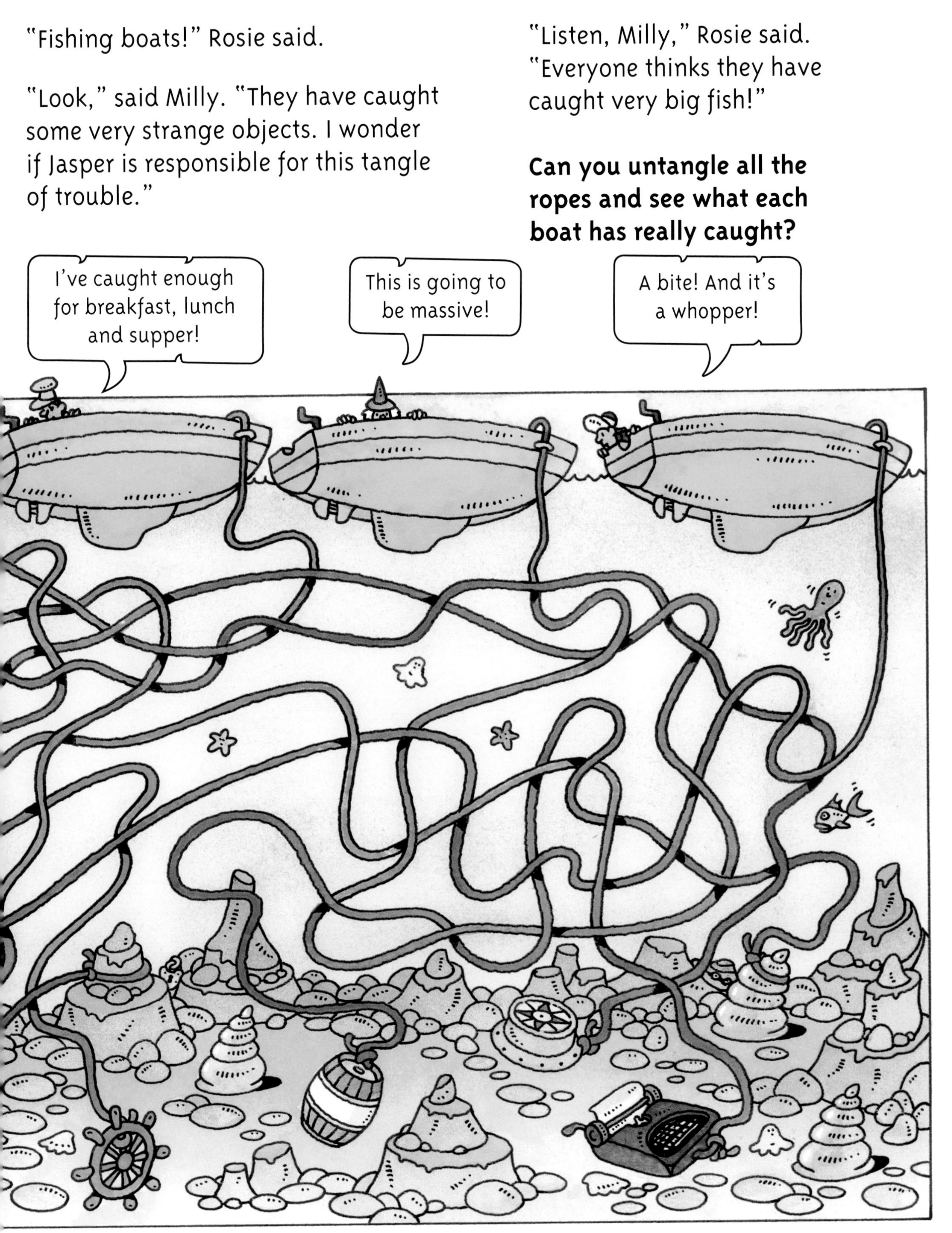

Shell searching

Milly and Rosie untangled the last of the ropes and the two friends headed on toward Jasper's lair. All the while they kept a lookout for some of Jasper's mischief.

They soon found it. A small group of underwater creatures huddled together looking very cold.

"Oh Milly," they cried. "Jasper has frightened us all out of our shells – and hidden them too. Can you help us find them? Our shells match our bodies."

Can you find all the lost shells?

Sharks!

The sea creatures wriggled back into their shells. Milly and Rosie waved goodbye.

"Jasper's probably home by now," Milly said. "We must get the crown back. If Jasper becomes King, Puzzle Ocean will be a terrible place to live."

Suddenly they saw large creatures circling around them. Sharks!

"The only thing Puzzle Ocean sharks like chomping better than mer-people are seaweed sandwiches," cried Milly. "Quick, Rosie! There are sure to be some lying around."

Can you find each shark a seaweed sandwich?

Spiky sandbank

The sharks swallowed the seaweed sandwiches and swam away. Milly and Rosie journeyed on to shallower water. Suddenly, ahead of them loomed the sandbank. Beyond it lay Jasper's lair. Rosie shivered. Now she was on her own...

"Head for the pink glow in the sky, Rosie," said Milly. "But be careful. The bank is made of squelchy sand. If you step in it you'll sink!"

Can you find a safe route across the sand bank to the pink glow?

SQUELCHY
SAND

A shadowy cave

Rosie scrambled safely to the other side of the sandbank. Here, the sand dipped away to the sea again. Rosie dived beneath the waves. She didn't have to swim long before she reached a shadowy cave. Was this where Jasper lived?

Cautiously, she peered inside. There was no sign of him, but Rosie saw several things which made her think it really was Jasper's cave. And then she spotted something which made her certain.

Could this be Jasper's cave?
What has Rosie spotted?

LOBSTER SLIPPERS

FLIPPER SLIPPER

My Pals
Mother
GRUB
How to make MISCHIEF!
A Fishnet DVD
SEAWEED POP
How to be KING
JAS
LOBSTER LOOT
LOBSTER LOOT

Rescue Rosie

There was no sign of Jasper. Quickly, Rosie lifted the golden crown down from its hiding place. But suddenly she heard a noise behind her. She turned around and found herself face to face with Jasper and his lobster pals!

"Ah ha! An intruder," Jasper smirked. "You're in trouble. I'm going to make you my prisoner!"

With that he lunged forward to grab Rosie and the crown.

Was this the end for Rosie?

Would she be trapped in Jasper's cave forever?

What do you think?

Milly's bargain

Silently, Milly scuttled up on the back of a spotted crab. She threw a big net over Jasper and the lobsters, and they were caught before they knew it!

"This friendly sea creature gave me a lift across the sandbank," Milly smiled.

"You'll never get away with this!" Jasper cackled.

…Milly's treasure was gone!

Do you know what Milly's treasure is? Can you find it here?

Fishy feast

Jasper and the lobsters were very happy with the pirate treasure. They were so busy trying it on that they didn't see Rosie and Milly sneak away with the golden crown.

The friendly crab gave Milly and Rosie a piggyback over the sandbank. Then the two friends swam on to the King of Puzzle Ocean's castle.

That evening, the King held a great feast to celebrate, and awarded Milly and Rosie special shell medals for being so brave. Rosie and Milly were very happy and danced with all their ocean friends.

How many ocean friends do you recognize at the party?

Yum, seaweed sandwiches
Jolly Jelly
Seaweed Sandwiches
Seaside Sausages
Ocean Surprise
Seafoam Slurps
Puzzle Pop
Puz Pop
Seaweed Sandwiches
Lobster Chocpot

Goodbye

After the feast it was time for Rosie to go.

"Keep your shimmery cobweb, Rosie," said Milly. "You never know when you might need it again."

"Thank you, Milly," said Rosie. "But there's one thing I don't understand..."

"...Why did you give the precious pirate treasure to Jasper?"

"The treasure wasn't so precious," Milly smiled. "Don't you remember the chest and the scrap of paper inside it?"

What did the paper say? **(Look back at page 235.)**

Answers

Pages 228-229
On the beach

Milly is here.

Milly is a mermaid!

Pages 230-231
Ocean trouble

Jasper is here.

Pages 232-233
Milly's plan
The things Milly needs are circled in black.

Pages 234-235
Underwater
The differences are circled in black.

Milly is here.

Pages 236-237
A fishy problem
The fish for the music class are circled in black. The fish for the juggling class are circled in red. The fish for the sports class are circled in blue. The fish for the art class are circled in yellow.

Pages 238-239
Overboard!

Pages 240-241
Shell searching
The lost shells are circled in black.

Pages 242-243
Sharks!
The seaweed sandwiches are circled in black.

Pages 244-245
Spiky sandbank
The safe route is shown in black.

Pages 246-247
A shadowy cave
Rosie has spotted the golden crown. The things that make Rosie think this is Jasper's cave are circled in black.

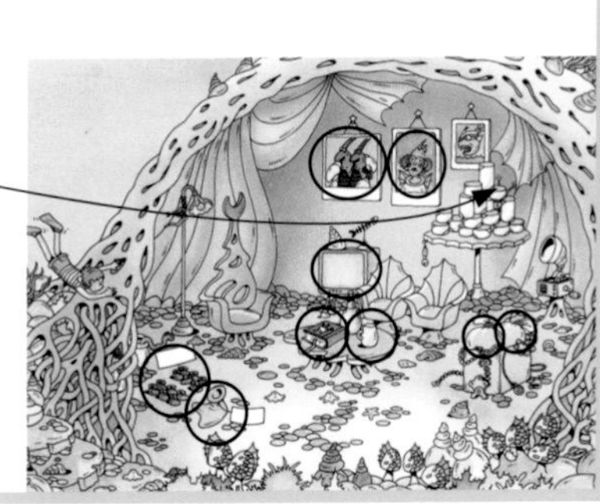

Pages 248-249
Rescue Rosie
Rosie has spotted Milly coming to her rescue.

Pages 250-251
Milly's bargain
Milly wants to give Jasper the Jolly Dodger treasure she picked up on the way. Here it is, all collected in the magic treasure-collecting bag.

Pages 252-253
Fishy feast
Look back through the book and see how many faces you recognize here.

Page 254
Goodbye
The paper said that the Jolly Dodger treasure was fake. This means it is not worth anything.

Did you spot everything?

Blue oysters

Jolly Dodger treasure

Yellow-clawed lobsters

The chart below shows you how many blue oysters are hiding on each double page. You can also find out which piece of Jolly Dodger treasure is hidden where.

Pages	Blue oysters	Jolly Dodger treasure
228-229	three	magic treasure-collecting bag
230-231	two	silver cutlass
232-233	three	precious perfume
234-235	one	pearl necklace
236-237	four	rum
238-239	three	gold locket
240-241	two	piece of eight
242-243	two	ruby ring
244-245	two	emerald eye patch
246-247	four	diamond dolphin
248-249	one	glass goblet
250-251	three	gem-encrusted telescope
252-253	three	emerald eye patch, gem-encrusted telescope, magic treasure-collecting bag, pearl necklace, ruby ring, rum

Did you remember to look out for Jasper's sneaky yellow-clawed lobster pals? Look back through the story again and see if you can spot them.

This edition first published in 2010 by Usborne Publishing Ltd., Usborne House, 83-85 Saffron Hill, London EC1N 8RT, England.

www.usborne.com
Copyright © 2010, 2003, 1996 Usborne Publishing Ltd.

The name Usborne and the devices are Trade Marks of Usborne Publishing Ltd. All rights reserved. No part of this publication may be reproduced, stored in a retrieval system or transmitted in any form or by any means, electronic, mechanical, photocopying, recording or otherwise, without the prior permission of the publisher. UE